Home Sweet Home

Home Sweet Home

Edited by Kathryn M. Patton

IDEALS PUBLICATIONS
NASHVILLE, TENNESSEE

ISBN 0-8249-5884-5

Published by Ideals Publications
A division of Guideposts
535 Metroplex Drive, Suite 250
Nashville, Tennessee 37211
www.idealsbooks.com

Color separations by Precision Color Graphics, Franklin, Wisconsin

Printed and bound in the USA by RR Donnelley

Library of Congress Cataloging-in-Publication Data

Home sweet home / edited by Kathryn M. Patton.
     p. cm.
  Includes index.
  ISBN 0-8249-5884-5 (alk. paper)
  1. Family—Literary collections. 2. Home—Literary collections. 3. American liter-
ature. I. Patton, Kathryn.
  PS509.F27H66 2005
  810.8'3552—dc22
                              2005005148

Publisher, Patricia A. Pingry
Book Editor, Kelly Riley Baugh
Art Director, Eve DeGrie
Copy Editor, Melinda Rathjen
Permissions Editor, Patsy Jay

Book Design by Eve DeGrie

Songs prepared by Dick Torrans, Melode Inc.

Images by Fine Art Photographic Library, London

10 9 8 7 6 5 4 3 2 1

ACKNOWLEDGMENTS

ALDRICH, BESS STREETER. "Small Town Home" and "Welcome Home" from *Ladies' Home Journal*, June and September 1933. Used with permission of the publisher. BUTLER, EDITH SHAW. "Prayer for a New House." Used by permission of Nancy B. Truesdell. FIELD, RUTH B. "Spring Journey." Used by permission of Natalie Field Bevis. GRIMMER, VIRGINIA BORMAN. "An Old Homeplace." Used by permission of Herman J. Grimmer. GUEST, EDGAR A. "The Perfect Dinner Table" and "The Little Home." Used by permission of M. Henry Sobell III. HOLMES, MARJORIE. "Friday Night" from *You and I and Yesterday*. Copyright © 1973, 1987 by Marjorie Holmes. Published by Doubleday. Used by permission of Dystel & Goderich Literary Management. HOLMES, REGINALD. "Family Reunion" and "Around the World with Dad." Used by permission of Shirley A. Radwick. HOOVER, DAN A. "A Father to His Flag." Used by permission of Carol Hoover Allen for Golde Hoover. MALLOCH, DOUGLAS. "Where Home Is" from *Come On Home* by Douglas Malloch; published in 1923 by George H. Doran Co. Used by permission of Lareda Anderson. SHARPE, ERNEST JACK. "Christmas At Grandma's." Used by permission of White Cloud Community Library. WILDER, LAURA INGALLS. "A Party At Grandma's" and "A Snug Prairie Home" from *Little House In the Big Woods*. Copyright © 1932 by Laura Ingalls Wilder, renewed 1959, 1987 by Roger Lea MacBride. Published by HarperTrophy, a division of HarperCollins Publishers. "Little Gray Home In the West" from *These Happy Golden Years* by Laura Ingalls Wilder. Copyright © 1943 and 1971 by Little House Heritage Trust. Published by HarperTrophy, a division of HarperCollins Publishers." GANNON & KENT MUSIC. "I'll Be Home For Christmas" by Walter Kent, Kim Gannon and Buck Ram. Copyright © 1939 (Renewed) by Gannon & Kent Music (ASCAP). International Copyright Secured. All Rights Reserved. Reprinted by permission.

Our sincere thanks to the following authors for permission to reprint: Bea Bourgeois for "Colored Eggs and Jelly Beans"; Nadine Brothers Lybarger for "The Quilting Bee"; M. M. Marshall for "A Loving Home"; Helen Whiteman Schick for "The Spell of Silver Bells"; Garnett Ann Schultz for "A Little Brown Cottage" and for "That Makes a House a Home"; Ruth H. Underhill for "The Old Porch Swing"; Barbara W. Weber for "Grandma's House."

Our sincere thanks to the following authors who submitted material to Ideals for publication, and whom we could not locate: Elsie Elaine Halsey for "Coffee Break"; Zenith Hess for "Home"; Eleanor Thompson for "Dreams of Childhood."

While every effort has been made to establish ownership and use of each selection in this book, this has not always been possible. If contacted, the publisher will be pleased to rectify any inadvertent errors or omissions in subsequent editions.

Table of Contents

Chapter One

A New Home

Building a Family

The crown of the home is godliness;
The beauty of the home is order;
The glory of the home is hospitality;
The blessing of the home is contentment.

—Henry Van Dyke

LITTLE GRAY HOME IN THE WEST

LAURA INGALLS WILDER

It was one of Ma's delicious dinners, but all the food tasted alike to Laura. Even the wedding cake was dry as sawdust in her mouth, for at last she realized that she was going away from home, that never would she come back to this house to stay. They all lingered at the table, for they knew that after dinner came the parting, but finally Almanzo said that it was time to go.

Laura put her bonnet on again and went out to the buggy as Almanzo drove to the door. There were goodbye kisses and good wishes, while he stood ready to help her into the buggy. But Pa took her hand.

"You'll help her from now on, young man," he said to Almanzo. "But this time, I will." Pa helped her into the buggy.

Ma brought a basket covered with a white cloth. "Something to help make your supper," she said, and her lips trembled. "Come back soon, Laura."

They drove over the road they had traveled so many times, across the neck of Big Slough, around the corner by Pearson's livery barn, up Main Street and across the railroad tracks, then out on the road toward the new house on Almanzo's tree claim.

The tracks of his wagon and buggy wheels had made a perfect half-circle drive curving into the grove of little sapling trees before the house. There the house sat, and it was neatly finished with siding and smoothly painted a soft gray. Its front door was comfortably in the middle, and two windows gave the whole house a smiling look. On the doorstep lay a large, brown shepherd dog, which rose and politely wagged to Laura as the buggy stopped.

"Hello, Shep!" Almanzo said. He helped Laura down and unlocked the door. "Go in while I put up the horses," he told her.

Just inside the door she stood and looked. This was the large room. Its

A New Home

TEN

walls were neatly plastered a soft white. At its far end stood a drop-leaf table, covered with Ma's red-checked tablecloth. A chair sat primly at either end of it. Beside it was a closed door.

In the center of the long wall at Laura's left, a large window let in southern sunshine. Companionably placed at either side of it, two rocking chairs faced each other. Beside the one nearest Laura stood a small round table, and above it a hanging lamp was suspended from the ceiling. Someone could sit there in the evening and read a paper, while in the other chair someone could knit.

The window beside the front door let more sunny light into that pleasant room.

Two closed doors were in the other long wall. Laura opened the one nearest her, and saw the bedroom. Her Dove-in-the-Window quilt was spread upon the wide bed, and her two feather pillows stood plumply at the head of it. Against the wall under the front window stood Laura's trunk.

She had seen all this quickly. Now she took off her poke bonnet and laid it on the shelf. She opened her trunk and took out a calico dress and apron. Taking off her black cashmere, she hung it carefully in the curtain closet, then slipped into the blue calico dress and tied on the crisply ruffled, pink apron. She went into the front room as Almanzo came into it through the door by the drop-leaf table.

"All ready for work, I see!" he said gaily, as he set Ma's basket on the chair near him. "Guess I'd better get ready for my work too." He turned at the bedroom door

to say, "Your Ma told me to open your bundle and spread things around."

Laura returned to the front room. She took up Ma's basket, and opened the last door. She knew it must be the pantry door, but she stood in surprise and then in delight, looking at that pantry. All one wall was covered with shelves and drawers, and a broad shelf was under a large window at the pantry's far end.

She took Ma's basket to that shelf, and opened it. There was a loaf of Ma's good bread, a ball of butter, and what had been left of the wedding cake. She left it all on the shelf while she investigated the pantry.

Beneath the shelf were many drawers of different sizes. Directly below the spices, and above the window shelf, were two rather narrow drawers. Laura found that

Someone could sit there in the evening and read a paper, while in the other chair someone could knit.

one was almost full of white sugar, and the other of brown sugar. How handy!

Next, a deep drawer was full of flour, and smaller ones held graham flour and cornmeal. You could stand at the window shelf and mix up anything, without stirring a step. Outside the window was the great, blue sky, and the leafy little trees.

Another deep drawer was filled with towels and tea towels. Another held two tablecloths and some napkins. A shallow one held knives and forks and spoons.

Carefully covering the ball of butter,

Laura carried it down the stairs into the cool, dark cellar, and set it on a hanging shelf that swung from the ceiling. She heard steps overhead, and as she came up the cellar stairs she heard Almanzo calling her name.

"I thought you were lost in this big house!" he said.

"I was putting the butter down in the cellar so it would keep cool," Laura said.

"Like your pantry?" he asked her, and she thought how many hours he must have worked to put up all those shelves and to make and fit those many drawers.

"Yes," she said.

"Then let's go look at Lady's big little colt. I want you to see the horses in their stalls, and the place I have fixed for your cow. She's picketed out to grass now, just out of reach of the young trees."

They explored the long stable and the yard beyond it. Almanzo showed her the new haystacks on the north, to shelter the yard and stable when the winter winds came. Laura petted the horses and the colt, and Shep as he followed close at her heels. They looked at the little maples and box elders and willows and cottonwoods.

Quickly, the afternoon was gone. It was time for chores and supper.

"Don't build a fire," Almanzo told her. "Set out that bread and butter your mother gave us; I'll milk Fawn, and we'll have bread and new milk for supper."

"And cake," Laura reminded him.

When they had eaten supper and washed the few dishes, they sat on the front doorstep as evening came. They heard Prince blow out his breath, *whoof!* as he lay down on his bed of clean hay in the stable. They saw the dim bulk of Fawn on the grass, where she lay chewing her cud and resting. Shep lay at their feet; already he was half Laura's dog.

Laura's heart was full of happiness. She knew she need never be homesick for the old home. It was so near that she could go to it whenever she wished, while she and Almanzo made the new home in their own little house.

All this was theirs: their own horses, their own cow, their own claim. The many leaves of their little trees rustled softly in the gentle breeze.

Twilight faded as the little stars went out and the moon rose and floated upward. Its silvery light flooded the sky and the prairie. The winds that had blown whispering over the grasses all the summer day now lay sleeping, and quietness brooded over the moon-drenched land.

"It is a wonderful night," Almanzo said.

"It is a beautiful world," Laura answered, and in memory she heard the voice of Pa's fiddle and the echo of a song:

> Golden years are passing by,
> These happy, golden years.

A New Home

THIRTEEN

LITTLE GRAY
HOME IN THE WEST

D. EARDLEY-WILMOT

HERMANN LÖHR

When the gold - en sun sinks in the hills,_____ and the

toil of a long day is o'er,_____ Though the

road may be long, in the lilt of a song I for -

get I was wea - ry be - fore._____ Far a -

-head, where the blue sha - dows fall,_____ I shall come to con - tent - ment and rest; And the toils of the day will be all charmed a - way in my lit - tle gray home of the west._____

To make a happy fireside clime
     To weans and wife,
That is the true pathos and sublime
     Of human life.
               —ROBERT BURNS

Prayer for a New House

EDITH SHAW BUTLER

Let this house shelter joy
     And dreams come true.
May someone love these rooms
     And keep them bright.
Let laughter and contentment
     Dwell here too
And children kneel to say
     Small prayers at night.
Perhaps there'll be
     A teakettle that sings
And scarlet blossoms
     On these windowsills;
A home is made
     Of just such little things.
Let someone love
     This view of distant hills.
Let firelight flicker
     On piano keys.
Let books and games
     And music have their part
And many, many shining
     Christmas trees
To warm the very cockles
     Of the heart.
Let such things weave
     A spell that will endear
This house to those
     So blessed as to live here.

Home Sweet Home

A New Home

That Makes a House a Home

GARNETT ANN SCHULTZ

It isn't curtains starched and fine,
Nor windows shining clean,
Expensive paintings on the walls
That catch the sunlight's gleam,
Nor furniture so new and grand,
The many things you own—
For not a single one of these
Can make a house a home.

It matters not a speck of dust;
To real folks this won't count,
Nor that you have the worldly things
In any large amount.
A house can never be a home
However hard you'd try,
Unless the welcome's friendly there—
A twinkle in your eye.

It takes a handshake firm and true,
A greeting warm and gay,
An air of love and happiness
As we would go our way;
'Tis these that make a house a home
Though worldly things are few,
And folks will always come again—
But just because of you.

A house can never be a home,
However long we live,
Unless it's filled with friendliness,
With laughter we can give.
Whatever else we chance to have,
How much we gain or own,
'Tis only people, real and true,
That make a house a home.

A New Home

THE NEWLYWEDS

CHARLES DICKENS

It was a strange condition of things, the honeymoon being

over and the bridesmaids gone home, when I found myself sitting down in my own small house with Dora; quite thrown out of employment, as I may say, in respect of the delicious old occupation of making love.

It seemed such an extraordinary thing to have Dora always there. It was so unaccountable not to be obliged to go out to see her, not to have any occasion to be tormenting myself about her, not to have to write to her, not to be scheming and devising opportunities of being alone with her. Sometimes of an evening, when I looked up from my writing, and saw her seated opposite, I would lean back in my chair, and think how queer it was that there we were alone together as a matter of course—nobody's business any more—all the romance of our engagement put away upon a shelf, to rust—no one to please but one another—one another to please, for life.

One of our first feats in the housekeeping way was a little dinner to Traddles. I met him in town, and asked him to walk out with me that afternoon. He readily consenting, I wrote to Dora, saying I would bring him home. It was pleasant weather, and on the road we made my domestic happiness the theme of conversation. Traddles was very full of it; and said that, picturing himself with such a home, and Sophy waiting and preparing for him, he could think of nothing wanting to complete his bliss.

I could not have wished for a prettier little wife at the opposite end of the table, but I certainly could have wished, when we sat down, for a little more room. I did not know how it was, but though there were only two of us, we were at once always cramped for room, and yet had always room enough to lose everything in.

I could not help wondering in my own mind, as I contemplated the boiled leg of mutton before me, previous to carving it, how it came to pass that our joints of meat were of such extraordinary shapes.

"My love," said I to Dora, "what have you got in that dish?"

I could not imagine why Dora had been making tempting little faces at me, as if she wanted to kiss me.

"Oysters, dear," said Dora, timidly.

"Was that *your* thought?" said I, delighted.

"Ye-yes, Doady," said Dora.

"There never was a happier one!" I exclaimed, laying down the carving-knife and fork. "There is nothing Traddles likes so much!"

"Ye-yes, Doady," said Dora, "and so I bought a beautiful little barrel of them, and the man said they were very good. But I-I am afraid there's something the matter with them. They don't seem right." Here Dora shook her head, and diamonds twinkled in her eyes.

"They are only opened in both shells," said I. "Take the top one off, my love."

"But it won't come off, said Dora, trying very hard, and looking very much distressed.

"Do you know, Copperfield," said Traddles, cheerfully examining the dish, "I think it is in consequence—they are capital oysters, but I think it is in consequence—of their never having been opened."

They never had been opened; and we had no oyster knives and couldn't have used them if we had; so we looked at the oysters and ate the mutton. At least we ate as much of it as was done, and made up

with capers. If I had permitted him, I am satisfied that Traddles would have made a perfect savage of himself, and eaten a plateful of raw meat, to express enjoyment of

the repast; but I would hear of no such immolation on the altar of friendship; and we had a course of bacon instead; there happening, by good fortune, to be cold bacon in the larder.

My poor little wife was in such affliction when she thought I should be annoyed, and in such a state of joy when she found I was not, that the discomfiture I had subdued very soon vanished, and we passed a happy evening—Dora sitting with her arm on my chair while Traddles and I discussed a glass of wine, and taking every opportunity of whispering in my ear that it was so good of me not to be a cruel, cross old boy. By and by she made tea for us, which it was so pretty to see her do, as if she was busying herself with a set of doll's tea things, that I was not particular about the quality of the beverage. Then Traddles and I played a game or two at cribbage; and, Dora singing to the guitar the while, it seemed to me as if our courtship and marriage were a tender dream of mine, and the night when I first listened to her voice were not yet over.

The treasures of the deep are not so precious as are the concealed comforts of a man locked up in woman's love: I scent the air of blessings when I come but near the house. ❧
—THOMAS MIDDLETON

A New Home

A Little Brown Cottage

Garnett Ann Schultz

Just a little brown cottage
You might never see,
All cozy and safe
Neath a wide, spreading tree,
A porch nodding welcome,
A door open wide,
And a heart full of love
When at last you're inside.

'Tis a bright little cottage,
So sparkling and gay,
All filled up with sunbeams
In the midst of the day,
A rocker so cozy,
A table, a chair,
And laughter abundant
That blesses you there.

'Tis a quaint little cottage,
Very simple, and yet
The moments I've spent there
I'll never forget;
There is so much of home
In this small, precious place
And so much kindness
On one loving face.

One little brown cottage
Such a treasure would seem,
At the end of the road
Nestled snug in a dream.
There's someone I love
Made this cottage a home.
Faith and love dwell here with her;
She is never alone.

A New Home

WELCOME HOME

BESS STREETER ALDRICH

Tell why you continue to live in a small town, wrote the editor. The question makes me stop and wonder. Perhaps it's inertia—just small-town stagnation. But I do not think so.

It is true I do not always stay here. Out of the twelve months of the past year, five of them were spent away—three on the West Coast and two in the pine-and-lake region of northern Minnesota. But my home is here. Good friends are here. I live and do my work here where the streets go unnamed, and the one train and one bus each way per day slip through town with few passengers, and the band lustily executes "Poet and Peasant" and "Under the Double Eagle March."

No one and no circumstances are compelling me to remain. In the eight years since my husband's death there has not been a day that I might not have packed the typewriter and moved to Lincoln or Omaha, my state's two largest cities, or to any big city east or west. Not that I depreciate the many advantages of living in one of them, but to me they are for visiting, and my little town for home.

It was just twenty-three years ago that, as a young married woman with a two-month-old baby girl in my arms, I arrived at the box-like station and was met by my husband, who had preceded me by a few weeks. I had not wanted to come to Nebraska. My earliest recollection of hearing the name of the state was a picture of my mother sending me over to the church basement with some old clothes and dried apples which she explained were to be sent to the poor folks out in Nebraska. The impression persisted, so that when my husband and my sister's husband negotiated for the purchase of the bank here, I was not at all enthusiastic about the move. I did not want to wear old clothes and I did not want to eat dried apples.

On the day on which we arrived there was a typical Nebraska dust storm of no modest or refined proportions under way. But my loyalty to the state of my adoption insists that I digress here and explain that the old

A New Home

TWENTY-EIGHT

windstorms are becoming less and less frequent. No doubt it is the diversified farming as it is practiced today which has steadied weather conditions in the Midwest. In the days when the hot winds blew from an unbroken expanse of stubble fields and barren lands, serious damage was done. But under modern conditions the landscape is broken with such regularity by crops still unmatured that serious damage from winds is no longer likely.

Si Maris, whom the menfolk had hired to meet us, was at the station with a two-seated surrey and team to take the women of the party up to the cottage that my husband had rented. Because the wind was blowing so hard that I would not trust my baby out of my arms, my husband and my brother-in-law wheeled the empty cab up to the house, while my sister, mother, the baby and I rode in state with Si. Si was not sure which of three cottages at the end of the street was the one Mr. Aldrich had rented, but it did not take me long to pick it out, for through the blasts of dust I could see my best upholstered rocking chair, a wedding present, sitting on a little porch with an arm hanging limply down at its side, evidently broken in shipping.

Through the gusts of dirt we hurried up to the little cottage, and it was then that I had my first taste of Nebraska small-town hospitality. Si's sister had come in to get the dinner, which was all ready for us. On my stove and with my own dishes she had prepared a delicious meal for the strangers, that they might feel welcome.

I have experienced it a thousand times since—that warm-hearted hospitality, loyal friendship, and deep sympathy of the small town.

The Cottage

ROBERT GRAVES

Here in turn succeed and rule
Carter, smith, and village fool,
Then again the place is known
As tavern, shop, and Sunday school;
Now somehow it's come to me
To light the fire and hold the key,
Here in Heaven to reign alone.

All the walls are white with lime,
Big blue periwinkles climb
And kiss the crumbling windowsill;
Snug inside I sit and rhyme,

Planning, poem, book, or fable,
At my darling beech-wood table
Fresh with bluebells from the hill.

Through the window I can see
Rooks above the cherry tree,
Sparrows in the violet bed,
Bramble bush and bumblebee,
And old red bracken smoulders still
Among boulders on the hill,
Far too bright to seem quite dead.

A New Home

ORANGE-MOLASSES GLAZED CHICKEN

3 cups orange juice
½ cup red-wine vinegar
¼ cup molasses
4 bone-in skinless chicken breast
    halves (about 1½ pounds)

Coarse salt
Ground pepper

Preheat oven to 400°F. In a large skillet, combine orange juice, ½ cup red-wine vinegar, and ¼ cup molasses. Boil over high heat, skimming foam occasionally, until mixture is reduced to ½ cup, 10 to 15 minutes. Reserve half of glaze for serving. Place chicken breast halves on a rimmed, foil-lined baking sheet. Season generously with salt and pepper; brush with glaze. Bake chicken, brushing with glaze twice during baking, until juices run clear when pierced, 35 to 40 minutes. Serve hot with reserved glaze. Makes 4 servings.

Company for Dinner

MASHED POTATOES WITH CARROTS AND LEEKS

2 pounds potatoes, peeled and cut into
    2-inch chunks
2 carrots, cut into ½-inch chunks
1 leek (white and pale green parts only),
    washed and coarsely chopped

¼ cup unsalted butter
¾ cup whole milk
¾ teaspoon salt
¼ teaspoon black pepper

In a large saucepan, cover potatoes with cold water. Bring to a boil, then reduce heat and simmer, uncovered, until tender (about 18 minutes). Drain and return to saucepan. While potatoes are simmering, boil carrots in salted water in a medium saucepan until just tender, 5 to 6 minutes. Drain. In a large skillet, sauté leek in butter over moderately low heat, stirring occasionally, until very tender, about 6 minutes. Add milk, salt, and pepper; simmer for 2 minutes, stirring often. Combine with potatoes and coarsely mash with a potato masher. Stir in carrots and serve warm. Makes 4 servings.

RED AND GREEN SALAD WITH BUTTERMILK DRESSING

½ cup finely chopped red onion
1 bunch red-leaf lettuce, torn into pieces
1 bunch watercress, coarse stems discarded
1 cup thinly sliced seedless cucumber
½ teaspoon minced garlic
¼ teaspoon salt
½ cup low-fat buttermilk

2 tablespoons low-fat sour cream
1 tablespoon mayonnaise
¼ teaspoon ground tarragon
¼ teaspoon dry mustard
Salt
Pepper

 Soak onion in 1 cup cold water for 10 minutes, then drain well. In a large bowl, toss lettuce, watercress, and cucumber. In a small bowl, mash garlic and ¼ teaspoon salt together to make a paste. Whisk in buttermilk, sour cream, mayonnaise, tarragon, and mustard. Sprinkle with salt and pepper to taste. Spoon dressing over salad and top with onion. Makes 4 servings.

QUICK AND EASY SPICE CAKE

2½ cups all-purpose flour
2 teaspoons pumpkin pie spice
1½ teaspoons baking soda
½ teaspoon salt
1¼ cups dark brown sugar

½ cup unsalted butter, melted and cooled
1 egg
1 cup buttermilk
1 cup chopped walnuts
Vanilla or rum raisin ice cream, optional

 Preheat oven to 350°F. In a medium bowl, blend flour, pumpkin pie spice, baking soda, and salt. In a large bowl, whisk dark brown sugar, butter, and egg until smooth. Stir in flour mixture alternately with buttermilk, beginning with flour mixture. Fold in nuts. Transfer batter to buttered and floured 8- x 8-inch metal baking pan. Bake until tester inserted in center comes out clean (about 1 hour). Cool slightly in pan on wire rack. Serve warm with ice cream. Makes 8 servings.

Savory fare for a couple and their guests to enjoy in their new home

Chapter Two

Family at Home

The Rhythm of Everyday Life

The happiest moments of my life
have been the few which I have passed
at home in the bosom of my family.

—THOMAS JEFFERSON

FRIDAY NIGHT

MARJORIE HOLMES

You could generally count on treats on Friday nights when the *Saturday Evening Post* arrived. Dad would stroll downtown after supper for a friendly game before the magazines were pitched off the 8:13. He was usually first in line when they were hauled over to the newsstand from the depot on a hand truck, generally pulled by Leo Baker. When Dad got home he smelled not only of cigars and the fat, shiny new magazine under his arm, but the big striped sack in his pocket. For his final stop would be the Candy Kitchen.

This was our night for reading aloud. Especially in winter when the hard-coal burner clucked and hissed and shed its rosy glow. Sometimes the sack would be stuffed with marshmallows, fluffy white cushions dusty with powdered sugar or brown with toasted coconut. Rejoicing, we would run for the long forks while Mother drew up the rockers and leafed through the pages. And while she and Dad picked the first story, we would open the isinglass door and roast the marshmallows over the coals.

More often the treat was an assortment of rich, mouth-melting bon-bons made fresh that day. Sprawled on the floor, we would give ourselves over to their bliss, while Mother's voice wove enchantment through the words of Jack London, Edna Ferber, William Hazlett Upson, Gene Stratton Porter, Booth Tarkington, Zane Grey. We suffered in the Klondike, won the Golden West, laughed until we rolled on the floor over the Earthworm tractors of Alexander Botts; we scared ourselves with mysteries and murders; our hearts broke with the exquisite pangs of love.

Outside, the wind might be howling; a few feet away our bedrooms would be stone-cold. But here in the snug circle of the family, here in the firelight, we were warm, safe, feasting on delight.

Family at Home

When Mother Reads Aloud

AUTHOR UNKNOWN

When Mother reads aloud, the past
Seems real as every day;
I hear the tramp of armies vast;
I see the spears and lances cast;
I join the thrilling fray;
Brave knights and ladies fair and proud
I meet when Mother reads aloud.

When Mother reads aloud, far lands
Seem very near and true;
I cross the desert's gleaming sands,
Or hunt the jungle's prowling bands,
Or sail the ocean blue;
Far heights, whose peaks the cold mists shroud,
I scale, when Mother reads aloud.

When Mother reads aloud, I long
For noble deeds to do—
To help the right, redress the wrong;
It seems so easy to be strong,
So simple to be true.
Oh, thick and fast the visions crowd
When Mother reads aloud.

A Loving Home

M. M. MARSHALL

A loving home is a lighthouse
With children safe and warm,
Refuge from the cold outside,
A port in time of storm,

A harbor for the family,
A haven in the night,
A beacon that burns brightly
To shed abroad its light.

When time has passed, the children leave
For shelters of their own.
May each be guided by the light
Of love in every home.

Family at Home

The Perfect Dinner Table

EDGAR A. GUEST

A tablecloth that's slightly soiled
Where greasy little hands have toiled;
The napkins kept in silver rings;
And only ordinary things
From which to eat; a simple fare;
And just the wife and kiddies there;
And while I serve, the clatter glad
Of little girl and little lad
Who have so very much to say
About the happenings of the day.

Our manners may not be the best;
Perhaps our elbows often rest
Upon the table, and at times
That very worst of dinner crimes,
That very shameful act, and rude,
Of speaking ere you've downed your food,
Too frequently, I fear, is done,
So fast the little voices run.
Yet why should table manners stay
Those tongues that have so much to say?

At many a table I have been
Where wealth and luxury were seen,
And I have dined in halls of pride
Where all the guests were dignified;
But when it comes to pleasure rare,
The perfect dinner table's where
No stranger's face is ever known:
The dinner hour we spend alone,
When little girl and little lad
Run riot telling things to Dad.

Family at Home

The Children's Hour

HENRY WADSWORTH LONGFELLOW

Between the dark and the daylight,
When the night is beginning to lower,
Comes a pause in the day's occupations
That is known as the Children's Hour.

I hear in the chamber above me
The patter of little feet,
The sound of a door that is opened,
And voices soft and sweet.

From my study I see in the lamplight,
Descending the broad hall stair,
Grave Alice, and laughing Allegra,
And Edith with golden hair.

A whisper, and then a silence:
Yet I know by their merry eyes
They are plotting and planning together
To take me by surprise.

A sudden rush from the stairway,
A sudden raid from the hall!
By three doors left unguarded
They enter my castle wall!

They climb up into my turret,
O'er the arms and back of my chair;
If I try to escape, they surround me;
They seem to be everywhere.

Happy are the families where the
government of parents is the reign
of affection, and obedience of the
children the submission of love.

—FRANCIS BACON

Home Sweet Home

Family at Home

At Home with Teddy Roosevelt

JACOB A. RIIS

We were steaming out past Centre Island, under the rugged
shore where Sagamore Hill lay hid among the foliage. The president stood at the rail surveying the scenes he loves. Here he had played as a boy, and dreamed a boy's dreams; here he had grown to manhood; here his children were growing up around him, happy and healthy boys and girls. We passed a sandy bluff sloping sheer into the sound from under its crown of trees.

"See," he said, pointing to it. "Cooper's Bluff! Three generations of Roosevelts have raced down its slope. We did, only yesterday."

Sagamore Hill is the family sanctuary, whither they come back in June with one long sigh of relief that their holiday is in sight, in which they may have one another. No longer to themselves, it is true. The president is not permitted to be alone even in his own home. But still they have days of seclusion, and nights—that greatest night in the year, when the President goes camping with the boys. How much it all meant to him I never fully realized till last election day, when I went with him home to vote. The sun shone so bright and warm, when he came out from among his old neighbors, who crowded around to shake hands, that a longing came over him for the old place, and we drove out to Sagamore Hill to catch a glimpse of it in its Indian-summer glory. Four dogs came bounding out with joyous barks and leaped upon him, and he caressed them and called them by name, each and every one, while they whined with delight—"Sailor-boy" was happiest of the lot, a big, clumsy, but loyal fellow, "of several good breeds," said the president, whimsically. They followed him around as he went from tree to tree, and from shrub to shrub, visiting with each one, admiring the leaf of this and the bark of that, as if they were personal friends. And so they were; for he had planted them all. Seeing him with them, I grasped the real meaning of the family motto, *Qui plantavit curabit*, that stands carved in the beam over the door looking north toward the hill with the cedars, where the soil

Home Sweet Home

Family at Home

FORTY-FOUR

is warm and full of white pebbles, and it is nice to lie in the grass when strawberries are ripe.

***

When we drove back to the village that November day, I caught him looking back once or twice toward the house in its bower of crimson shrubs, and I saw that his heart was there. You would not wonder if you knew it. I never go away from Sagamore Hill without a feeling that if I lived there I would never leave it, and that nothing would tempt me to exchange it for the White House, with all it stands for. But then I am ten years older than Theodore Roosevelt; though it isn't always the years that count. For I think if it came to a vote, the children would carry my proposition with a shout. Not that Sagamore Hill has anything to suggest a palace. Quite the contrary: it is a very modest home for the president of the United States. On a breezy hilltop overlooking field and forest and sound, with the Connecticut shore on the northern horizon, its situation is altogether taking. The house is comfortable, filled with reminders of the stirring life its owner has led in camp and on the hunting trail, and with a broad piazza on the side that catches the cool winds of summer. But it is homelike rather than imposing. It is the people themselves who put the stamp upon it—the life they live there together.

***

The president himself teaches his boys how to shoot; he swims with them in the cove and goes with them on long horseback rides, starting sometimes before sunrise.

On fine days, as often as he can get away, luncheon is packed in the rowboat and he takes the whole family rowing to some distant point on the shore, which even the Secret Service men have not discovered, and there they spend the day, the president pulling the oars going and coming. Or else he takes Mrs. Roosevelt alone on a little jaunt, and these two, over whose honeymoon the years have no dominion, have a day to themselves, from which he returns to wrestle with powers and principalities and postmasters with twice the grip he had before; for she is truly his helpmeet and as wise as she is gentle and good.

The great day is when he goes camping

It is the people themselves who put the stamp upon it—the life they live there together.

with the boys. The Sagamore Hill boys and their cousins whose summer homes are near plan it for months ahead. A secluded spot alongshore is chosen, with good water and a nice sand beach handy, and the expedition sets out with due secrecy, the White House guardsmen being left behind to checkmate the reporters and the camera fiends. Mr. Roosevelt is sailing master and chief of the jolly band. Along in the afternoon they reach their hiding place; then bait and fishing poles are got ready—for they are real campers-out, not make-believes, and though they have grub on board, fish they must. When they have caught enough, the boys bring wood and build a fire. The president rolls up his sleeves and turns cook.

Afterward, they sit around the fire,

Family at Home

wrapped in blankets, and tell bear stories and ghost stories, while the children steal furtive glances at the shadows closing in upon the circle of flickering light. They are not afraid, those children. The word is not in the Sagamore Hill dictionary. The spectacle of little Archie, hatless, guiding a stalwart Rough Rider through the twilight woods, telling him to follow his white head and not be afraid of bogies—they won't hurt him—is a joy to me forever. But when owls are hooting in the dark woods I like to hug the fire myself. It feels twice as good then.

When the stars shine out in the sky overhead, they stretch themselves with their feet to the fire, roll up in their blankets, and sleep the untroubled sleep of the woods. The sun, peeping over the trees, finds them sporting in the cool, salt water; and long before the day begins for the world of visitors they are back home, a happy, roistering crew.

The Roosevelts have found (if they have not always had it; certainly the president's father did) the secret that binds families together with bonds which nothing can break: they are children with their boys and girls.

It was the policy of the good old gentleman to make his children feel that home was the happiest place in the world; and I value this delicious home-feeling as one of the choicest gifts a parent can bestow.
—WASHINGTON IRVING

Home Sweet Home

Family at Home

FORTY-EIGHT

Nurse's Song

WILLIAM BLAKE

When the voices of children are heard on the green,
And laughing is heard on the hill,
My heart is at rest within my breast,
And everything else is still.

"Then come home, my children, the sun is gone down,
And the dews of night arise;
Come, come, leave off play, and let us away,
Till the morning appears in the skies."

"No, no, let us play, for it is yet day,
And we cannot go to sleep;
Besides, in the sky the little birds fly,
And the hills are all cover'd with sheep."

"Well, well, go and play till the light fades away,
And then go home to bed."
The little ones leaped, and shouted, and laughed,
And all the hills echoed.

My Bed Is a Boat

ROBERT LOUIS STEVENSON

My bed is like a little boat;
    Nurse helps me in when I embark;
She girds me in my sailor's coat
    And starts me in the dark.

At night, I go on board and say
    Good night to all my friends on shore;
I shut my eyes and sail away
    And see and hear no more.

And sometimes things to bed I take,
    As prudent sailors have to do;
Perhaps a slice of wedding cake,
    Perhaps a toy or two.

All night across the dark we steer;
    But when the day returns at last,
Safe in my room, beside the pier,
    I find my vessel fast.

Family at Home

Sweet and Low

Alfred, Lord Tennyson

Joseph Barnby

Good Night
JANE TAYLOR

Little baby, lay your head
On your pretty cradle-bed;
Shut your eye-peeps, now the day
And the light are gone away;
All the clothes are tucked in tight;
Little baby dear, good night.

Yes, my darling, well I know
How the bitter wind doth blow;
And the winter's snow and rain
Patter on the window pane:
But they cannot come in here,
To my little baby dear;

For the window shutteth fast,
Till the stormy night is past;
And the curtains warm are spread
Round about her cradle-bed:
So till morning shineth bright,
Little baby dear, good night.

It takes a mother's love
To make a house a home,
A place to be remembered,
No matter where we roam.
—HELEN STEINER RICE

Home Sweet Home

Family at Home

A Snug Prairie Home

Laura Ingalls Wilder

The first snow came, and the bitter cold. The snow kept coming till it was drifted and banked against the house. In the mornings the window panes were covered with frost in beautiful pictures of trees and flowers and fairies.

Laura and Mary helped Ma with the work. Every morning there were the dishes to wipe. Mary wiped more of them than Laura because she was bigger, but Laura always wiped carefully her own little cup and plate.

By the time the dishes were all wiped and set away, the trundle bed was aired. Then, standing one on each side, Laura and Mary straightened the covers, tucked them in well at the foot and the sides, plumped up the pillows, and put them in place. Then Ma pushed the trundle bed into its place under the big bed.

After this was done, Ma began the work that belonged to that day. Each day had its own proper work. Ma used to say:

> Wash on Monday,
> Iron on Tuesday,
> Mend on Wednesday,
> Churn on Thursday,
> Clean on Friday,
> Bake on Saturday,
> Rest on Sunday.

Laura liked the churning and the baking days best of all the week.

In winter the cream was not yellow as it was in summer, and butter churned from it was white and not so pretty. Ma liked everything on her table to be pretty, so in the wintertime she colored the butter.

After she had put the cream in the tall crockery churn and set it near the stove to warm, she washed and scraped a long orange-colored carrot. Then she grated it on the bottom of the old, leaky tin pan that Pa had punched full of nail-holes for her. Ma rubbed the carrot across the roughness until she had rubbed it all through the holes, and when she

W. E. Hine

Family at Home

lifted up the pan, there was a soft, juicy mound of grated carrot.

She put this in a little pan of milk on the stove; and when the milk was hot, she poured milk and carrot into a cloth bag. Then she squeezed the bright yellow milk into the churn, where it colored all the cream. Now the butter would be yellow.

Laura and Mary were allowed to eat the carrot after the milk had been squeezed out. Mary thought she ought to have the larger share because she was older, and Laura said she should have it because she was littler. But Ma said they must divide it evenly. It was very good.

When the cream was ready, Ma scalded the long wooden churn-dash, put it in the churn, and dropped the wooden

But the best time of all was at night, when Pa came home.

churn-cover over it. The churn cover had a little round hole in the middle, and Ma moved the dash up and down, up and down, through the hole.

At first the splashes of cream showed thick and smooth around the little hole. After a long time, they began to look grainy. Then Ma churned more slowly, and on the dash there began to appear tiny grains of yellow butter.

When Ma took off the churn cover, there was the butter in a golden lump, drowning in the buttermilk. Then Ma took out the lump with a wooden paddle, into a wooden bowl, and she washed it many times in cold water, turning it over and

over and working it with the paddle until the water ran clear. After that she salted it.

Now came the best part of the churning. Ma molded the butter. On the loose bottom of the wooden butter mold was carved the picture of a strawberry with two strawberry leaves.

With the paddle Ma packed butter tightly into the mold until it was full. Then she turned it upside down over a plate, and pushed on the handle of the loose bottom. The little, firm pat of golden butter came out, with the strawberry and its leaves molded on the top.

Laura and Mary watched, breathless, one on each side of Ma, while the golden little butter pats, each with its strawberry on top, dropped onto the plate as Ma put all the butter through the mold. Then Ma gave them each a drink of good, fresh buttermilk.

On Saturdays, when Ma made the bread, they each had a little piece of dough to make into a little loaf. They might have a bit of cookie dough too, to make little cookies, and once Laura even made a pie in her patty pan.

After the day's work was done, Ma sometimes cut paper dolls for them. She cut the dolls out of stiff white paper, and drew the faces with a pencil. Then from bits of colored paper she cut dresses and hats, ribbons and laces, so that Laura and Mary could dress their dolls beautifully.

But the best time of all was at night, when Pa came home.

He would come in from his tramping through the snowy woods with tiny icicles hanging on the ends of his mustache. He

FIFTY-SEVEN

Alfred W Strutt

would hang his gun on the wall over the door, throw off his fur cap and coat and mittens, and call: "Where's my little half-pint of sweet cider half drunk up?"

That was Laura, because she was so small.

Laura and Mary would run to climb on his knees and sit there while he warmed himself by the fire. Then he would put on his coat and cap and mittens again and go out to do the chores and bring in plenty of wood for the fire.

All alone in the Big Woods and the snow and the cold, the little log house was warm and snug and cozy. Pa and Ma and Mary and Laura and Baby Carrie were comfortable and happy there, especially at night.

Then the fire was shining on the hearth, the cold and the dark and the wild beasts were all shut out, and Jack the brindle bulldog and Black Susan the cat lay blinking at the flames in the fireplace.

Home, the spot of earth supremely blest,
A dearer, sweeter spot than all the rest.
—ROBERT MONTGOMERY

Family at Home

HAMBURGER PIE

1 10-ounce package frozen
   mixed vegetables
1 pound ground beef
½ cup chopped onion
1 10¾-ounce can condensed
   tomato soup

1 teaspoon Worcestershire sauce
¼ teaspoon dried thyme, crushed
¼ teaspoon pepper
   Instant mashed potatoes,
    enough for four servings
   Paprika

Preheat oven to 375°F. Run cold water over vegetables to separate; drain. In a large skillet, brown meat with onion. Drain. Stir vegetables and ¼ cup water into skillet. Cook, covered, 5 to 10 minutes or until tender. Stir in soup, Worcestershire sauce, thyme, and pepper. Transfer to a 1½-quart casserole dish. Prepare potatoes according to package directions. Drop in mounds over hot mixture. If desired, sprinkle with paprika. Bake 25 to 30 minutes or until hot. Makes 4 servings.

HAM-POTATO SCALLOP

1½ cups cubed fully cooked ham, divided
½ cup chopped onion, divided
4 medium potatoes, peeled and thinly
   sliced, divided
1 10¾-ounce can condensed
   Cheddar cheese soup

½ cup milk
¼ teaspoon pepper
¼ cup fine dry bread crumbs
2 tablespoons snipped parsley
1 tablespoon butter, melted

Preheat oven to 350°F. In a 1½-quart casserole dish, layer half of the ham, half of the onion, and half of the potatoes. Repeat layers. In a medium bowl, combine soup, milk, and pepper, mixing well. Pour over potatoes. Bake covered about 1 hour or until potatoes are almost tender. In a small bowl, mix together bread crumbs, parsley, and butter. Sprinkle over casserole. Bake uncovered 15 minutes more. Let stand 10 minutes. Makes 4 servings.

TUNA AND CHIPS CASSEROLE

2 10½-ounce cans cream of mushroom soup
1 cup milk
2 7-ounce cans tuna, drained and flaked
2½ cups crushed potato chips
2 cups cooked green peas, drained

Preheat oven to 350°F. Pour soup into a 2-quart baking dish. Add milk and mix well. Add tuna, 2 cups potato chips, and peas; mix lightly. Sprinkle remaining potato chips over top. Bake 25 minutes, until heated through. Makes 6 to 8 servings.

BAKED MACARONI AND CHEESE

2 cups elbow macaroni
3 tablespoons butter
1 small onion, finely chopped
3 tablespoons all-purpose flour
2 cups milk

2 teaspoons whole-grain mustard
2 cups grated sharp Cheddar cheese, divided
Salt
Pepper
1 cup fresh bread crumbs

Preheat oven to 350°F. Add macaroni to rapidly boiling salted water. Cook until al dente. Rinse and drain. In a large pan, melt butter over low heat. Add onion and sauté 5 minutes, or until softened. Stir in flour and cook for 1 minute, or until pale and foaming. Remove from heat and gradually whisk in milk. Return to heat and simmer gently, stirring often, for 15 minutes. Remove from heat and stir in mustard. Add about 1¾ cups cheese, mixing well. Season with salt and pepper to taste. Stir pasta into cheese sauce. Spoon into greased 2-quart casserole dish and sprinkle remaining cheese and bread crumbs over top. Bake 15 minutes, or until golden brown and bubbling. Let stand 5 minutes. Makes 4 servings.

Tasty main dishes for a casual meal around the dinner table

Where Home Is

DOUGLAS MALLOCH

We have a cottage by the lake,
    A cabin in the hills;
And now and then the car we take
    And feel the gypsy thrills
Of tenting here and tenting there,
The joy of camping anywhere.

Of "home" one night the baby spoke;
    And then, the babe to tease
(For dads must have their little joke),
    I asked her, "If you please,
I'd like to have you tell me what
Is really home—you have a lot:

"You have Muskegon, by the shore,
    And Estes, where you climb;
And there's the tent, intended for
    A home at any time;
And there's the house we live in too—
Now, which is really 'home' to you?"

She looked at me with open eyes,
    In infant innocence,
And said with something of surprise—
    A father is so dense
In asking questions such as his—
"Why, home's wherever Mama is!"

And always it will be the same;
    Her heart the home will be.
She keeps the lamp of love aflame
    For wanderers to see.
However far her children roam,
Wherever Mother is, is home.

Family at Home

The Path to Home

EDGAR A. GUEST

There's the mother at the doorway
And the children at the gate
And the little parlor windows
With the curtains white and straight.

There are shaggy asters blooming
In the bed that lines the fence,
And the simplest of the blossoms
Seems of mighty consequence.

Oh, there isn't any mansion
Underneath God's starry dome
That can rest a weary pilgrim
Like the little place called home.

Men have sought for gold and silver;
Men have dreamed at night of fame;
In the heat of youth they've struggled
For achievement's honored name;

But the selfish crowns are tinsel,
And their shining jewels paste,
And the wine of pomp and glory
Soon grows bitter to the taste.

For there's never any laughter,
Howsoever far you roam,
Like the laughter of the loved ones
In the happiness of home.

There is nothing so important
As the mother's lullabies,
Filled with peace and sweet contentment,
When the moon begins to rise—

Nothing real except the beauty
And the calm upon her face
And the shouting of the children
As they scamper round the place.

For the greatest of man's duties
Is to keep the loved ones glad
And to have his children glory
In the father they have had.

So where'er a man may wander
And whatever be his care,
You'll find his soul still stretching
To the home he left somewhere.

You'll find his dreams all tangled
Up with hollyhocks in bloom
And the feet of little children
That go racing through a room

With the happy mother smiling
As she watches them at play—
These are all in life that matter,
When you've stripped the sham away.

Who loves the rain and loves his home, and looks
on life with quiet eyes, him will I follow through
the storm and at his hearth-fire keep me warm.

—FRANCES SHAW

Home Sweet Home

Isabel Naftel
1881.

Family at Home

Chapter Three

Gatherings at Home

Special Times Spent Together

When friends are at your hearthside met,
Sweet courtesy has done its most
If you have made each guest forget
That he himself is not the host.

—THOMAS BAILEY ALDRICH

A Happy Birthday

Louisa May Alcott

The twelfth of October was Rose's birthday, but no

one seemed to remember that interesting fact, and she felt delicate about mentioning it, so she fell asleep the night before wondering if she would have any presents. That question was settled early the next morning, for she was awakened by a soft tap on her face, and opening her eyes she beheld a little black-and-white figure sitting on her pillow, staring at her with a pair of round eyes very like blueberries, while one downy paw patted her nose to attract her notice. It was Kitty Comet, the prettiest of all pussies, and Comet evidently had a mission to perform, for a pink bow adorned her neck, and a bit of paper was pinned to it bearing the words, "For Miss Rose, from Frank."

That pleased her extremely, and that was only the beginning of the fun, for surprises and presents kept popping out in the most delightful manner all through the day, the Atkinson girls being famous jokers and Rose a favorite. But the best gift of all came on the way to Mount Windy-Top, where it was decided to picnic in honor of the great occasion. Three jolly loads set off soon after breakfast, for everybody went, and every-body seemed bound to have an extra good time, especially Mother Atkinson, who wore a hat as broad-brimmed as an umbrella, and took the dinner-horn to keep her flock from straying away.

A general scramble among the rocks was followed by a regular gypsy lunch, which the young folks had the rapture of helping to prepare. Mother Atkinson put on her apron, turned up her sleeves, and fell to work as gaily as if in her own kitchen, boiling the kettle slung on three sticks over a fire of cones and fir boughs; while the girls spread the mossy table with a feast of country goodies, and the children tumbled about in everyone's way till the toot of a horn made them settle down like a flock of hungry birds.

As soon as the merry meal and a brief interval of repose were over, it was unanimously voted to have some charades. A smooth, green spot

Gatherings at Home

between two stately pines was chosen for the stage; shawls were hung up, properties collected, audience and actors separated; and a word was quickly chosen.

The first scene discovered Mac in a despondent attitude and shabby dress, evidently much troubled in mind. To him entered a remarkable creature with a brown paper bag over its head. A little pink nose peeped through one hole in the middle, white teeth through another, and above two eyes glared fiercely. Spires of grass stuck in each side of the mouth seemed meant to represent whiskers; the upper corners of the bag were twisted like ears, and no one could doubt for a moment that the black scarf pinned on behind was a tail.

This singular animal seemed in pantomime to be comforting his master and offering advice, which was finally acted upon, for Mac pulled off his boots, helped the little beast into them, and gave him a bag; then, kissing his paw with a hopeful gesture, the creature retired, purring so successfully that there was a general cry of "Cat, puss, boots!"

"*Cat* is the word," replied a voice, and the curtain fell.

* * *

Rose took part in all the fun; she excused herself from the games in the evening, however, and sat talking to Uncle Alec in a lively way that both amazed and delighted him; for she confided to him that she played horse with the children, drilled with the light infantry, climbed trees, and did other dreadful things that would have caused the aunts to cry aloud if they knew of them.

"I don't care a pin what they say if you don't mind, Uncle," she answered, when he pictured the dismay of the good ladies.

"Ah, it's all very well to defy *them*, but you are getting so rampant, I'm afraid you will defy me next, and then where are we?"

"No, I won't! I shouldn't dare; because you are

Gatherings at Home

my guardian, and can put me in a straitjacket if you like"; and Rose laughed in his face, even while she nestled closer with a confiding gesture pleasant to see.

"Upon my word, Rosy, I begin to feel like the man who bought an elephant, and then didn't know what to do with him. I thought I had got a pet and plaything for years to come; but here you are growing up like a beanstalk, and I shall find I've got a strong-minded little woman on my hands before I can turn round. There's a predicament for a man and an uncle!"

***

When Rose went to bed, she found that Uncle

Home Sweet Home

Alec had not forgotten her; for on the table stood a delicate little easel, holding two miniatures set in velvet. She knew them both, and stood looking at them till her eyes brimmed over with tears that were both sweet and sad; for they were the faces of her father and mother, beautifully copied from portraits fast fading away.

Presently she knelt down, and, putting her arms round the little shrine, kissed one after the other, saying with an earnest voice, "I'll truly try to make them glad to see me by and by."

And that was Rose's little prayer on the night of her fourteenth birthday.

Gatherings at Home

The Little Home

EDGAR A. GUEST

The little house is not too small
To shelter friends who come to call.
Though low the roof and small its space,
It holds the Lord's abounding grace;
And every simple room may be
Endowed with happy memory.

The little house, severely plain,
A wealth of beauty may contain.
Within it those who dwell may find
High faith which makes for peace of mind,
And that sweet understanding which
Can make the poorest cottage rich.

The little house can hold all things
From which the soul's contentment springs.
'Tis not too small for love to grow,
For all the joys that mortals know,
For mirth and song and that delight
Which make the humblest dwelling bright.

Come in the Evening

THOMAS OSBORNE DAVIS

Come in the evening,
    or come in the morning;
Come when you're look'd for,
    or come without warning:
Kisses and welcome
    you'll find here before you,
And the oftener you come here
    the more I'll adore you!

The Country Mouse and the City Mouse

RICHARD SCRAFTON SHARPE

In a snug little cot lived a fat little mouse,
Who enjoyed, unmolested, the range of the house;
With plain food content, she would breakfast on cheese;
She dined upon bacon and supped on grey peas.

A friend from the town to the cottage did stray,
And he said he was come a short visit to pay;
So the mouse spread her table as gay as you please,
And brought the nice bacon and charming grey peas.

The visitor frowned, and he thought to be witty:
Cried he, "You must know, I am come from the city,
Where we all should be shocked at provisions like these,
For we never eat bacon and horrid grey peas.

"To town come with me, I will give you a treat:
Some excellent food, most delightful to eat.
With me shall you feast just as long as you please;
Come, leave this fat bacon and shocking grey peas."

This kind invitation she could not refuse,
And the city mouse wished not a moment to lose;
Reluctant she quitted the fields and the trees,
The delicious fat bacon and charming grey peas.

They were nicely regaling, when into the room
Came the dog and the cat, and the maid with a broom:
They jumped in a custard both up to their knees;
The country mouse sighed for her bacon and peas.

Cried she to her friend, "Get me safely away,
I can venture no longer in London to stay;
For if oft you receive interruptions like these,
Give me my nice bacon and charming grey peas.

"Your living is splendid and gay, to be sure,
But the dread of disturbance you ever endure;
I taste true delight in contentment and ease,
And I feast on fat bacon and charming grey peas."

Home Sweet Home

SEVENTY-SEVEN

Gatherings at Home

THE BOWDEN REUNION

SARAH ORNE JEWETT

It is very rare in country life, where high days and holidays are few, that any occasion of general interest proves to be less than great. Such is the hidden fire of enthusiasm in the New England nature that, once given an outlet, it shines forth with almost volcanic light and heat. In quiet neighborhoods such inward force does not waste itself upon those petty excitements of every day that belong to cities, but when, at long intervals, the altars to patriotism, to friendship, to the ties of kindred, are reared in our familiar fields, then the fires glow, the flames come up as if from the inexhaustible burning heart of the earth; the primal fires break through the granite dust in which our souls are set. Each heart is warm and every face shines with the ancient light. Such a day as this has transfiguring powers, and easily makes friends of those who have been cold-hearted, and gives to those who are dumb their chance to speak, and lends some beauty to the plainest face.

"Oh, I expect I shall meet friends today that I haven't seen in a long while," said Mrs. Blackett with deep satisfaction. "Today will bring out a good many of the old folks, 'tis such a lovely day. I'm always glad not to have them disappointed."

We watched the boats drop their sails one by one in the cove as we drove along the high land. The old Bowden house stood, low-storied and broad-roofed, in its green fields as if it were a motherly brown hen waiting for the flock that came straying toward it from every direction. The first Bowden settler had made his home there, and it was still the Bowden farm; five generations of sailors and farmers and soldiers had been its children. And presently Mrs. Blackett showed me the stone-walled burying-ground that stood like a little fort on a knoll overlooking the bay, but, as she said, there were plenty of scattered Bowdens who were not laid there, some lost at sea, and some out West, and some who died in the war; most of the home graves were those of women.

We could see now that there were different footpaths from alongshore

Home Sweet Home

Gatherings at Home

EIGHTY

and across country. In all these there were straggling processions walking in single file, like old illustrations of *The Pilgrim's Progress*. There was a crowd about the house as if huge bees were swarming in the lilac bushes. Beyond the fields and cove a higher point of land ran out into the bay, covered with woods which must have kept away much of the northwest wind in winter. Now there was a pleasant look of shade and shelter there for the great family meeting.

* * *

The grove was so large that the great family looked far smaller than it had in the open field; there was a thick growth of dark pines and firs with an occasional maple or oak that gave a gleam of color like a bright window in the great roof. On three sides we could see the water, shining behind the tree trunks, and feel the cool salt breeze that began to come up with the tide just as the day reached its highest point of heat. We could see the green sunlit field we had just crossed as if we looked out at it from a dark room, and the old house and its lilacs standing placidly in the sun, and the great barn with a stockade of carriages from which two or three caretaking men who had lingered were coming across the field together. Mrs. Todd had taken off her warm gloves and looked the picture of content.

There never was a more generous out-of-door feast along the coast than the Bowden family set forth that day. To call it a picnic would make it seem trivial. The great tables were edged with pretty oak-leaf trimming, which the boys and girls made. We brought flowers from the fence-thickets of the great field; and out of the disorder of

flowers and provisions suddenly appeared as orderly a scheme for the feast as the marshal had shaped for the procession. I began to respect the Bowdens for their inheritance of good taste and skill and a certain pleasing gift of formality. Something made them do all these things in a finer way than most country people would have done them. As I looked up and down the tables there was a good cheer, a grave soberness that shone with pleasure, a humble dignity of bearing. There were some who should have sat below the salt for lack of this good breeding; but they were not many.

The leave-takings were as affecting as the meetings of these old friends had been. There were enough young persons at the reunion, but it is the old who really value

The leave-takings were as affecting as the meetings of these old friends had been.

such opportunities; as for the young, it is the habit of every day to meet their comrades—the time of separation has not come. To see the joy with which these elder kinsfolk and acquaintances had looked in one another's faces, and the lingering touch of their friendly hands; to see these affectionate meetings and then the reluctant partings, gave one a new idea of the isolation in which it was possible to live in that after all thinly settled region. They did not expect to see one another again very soon; the steady, hard work on the farms, the difficulty of getting from place to place, especially in winter when boats were laid up, gave double value to any occasion which could bring

a large number of families together. Even funerals in this country of the pointed firs were not without their social advantages and satisfactions. I heard the words "next summer" repeated many times, though summer was still ours and all the leaves were green.

The boats began to put out from shore, and the wagons to drive away. Mrs. Blackett took me into the old house when we came back from the grove: it was her father's birthplace and early home, and she had spent much of her own childhood there with her grandmother. She spoke of those days as if they had but lately passed; in fact, I could imagine that the house looked almost exactly the same to her. I could see the brown rafters of the unfinished roof as I looked up the steep staircase, though the best room was as handsome with its good wainscoting and touch of ornament on the cornice as any old room of its day in a town.

Some of the guests who came from a distance were still sitting in the best room when we went in to take leave of the master and mistress of the house. We all said eagerly what a pleasant day it had been, and how swiftly the time had passed. Perhaps it is the great national anniversaries which our country has lately kept, and the soldiers' meetings that take place everywhere, which have made reunions of every sort the fashion. This one, at least, had been very interesting. I fancied that old feuds had been overlooked, and the old saying that blood is thicker than water had again proved itself true.

Family Reunion

REGINALD HOLMES

It's family reunion time,
And folks from miles away
Will meet again to celebrate
Their very special day.
It's now the time for shaking hands,
For smiles, and also tears,
When folks are meeting relatives
They haven't seen for years.

There's Auntie Bea and Cousin Sue
And Walter, John, and Will;
There's Cousin Janie and boyfriend;
And there comes Uncle Phil.
There are lots of lovely nieces
With nephews by the score,
And at least a dozen babies
We haven't seen before.

It's when old folks get together
Away from toil and care,
And the youngsters are discussing
The hopes and dreams they share.
It's the day when troubles vanish,
A time to laugh and sing
While the ladies load the tables
With food fit for a king.

There is ham and mashed potatoes,
Baked beans, and apple pie;
Spice cake and fluffy biscuits,
So tempting to the eye.
Then comes the time for parting;
We wend our homeward way;
But what could be more wonderful
Than our reunion day?

EIGHTY-FIVE

MINT TEA PUNCH

3 cups water	½ teaspoon cinnamon
2 black-tea bags	¼ teaspoon nutmeg
1 cup fresh mint leaves	1½ cups orange juice
4 tablespoons sugar	1½ cups cranberry juice

 In a medium saucepan, bring water just to a boil. Remove from heat. Add tea bags and mint leaves. Allow to steep for five minutes. Remove tea bags and strain mint leaves. Stir in sugar, nutmeg, and cinnamon. In a large pitcher, combine orange juice and cranberry juice. Add tea and stir. Refrigerate until well-chilled (1–2 hours). Serve in a tall glass with ice and a sprig of mint. Makes 4 servings.

Party Luncheon Favorites

SEVEN-LAYER SALAD

1 medium head romaine or iceberg lettuce, shredded	4 hard-boiled eggs, sliced
1 cup chopped celery	1 cup mayonnaise
1 cup coarsely chopped green pepper	½ cup sour cream or plain low-fat yogurt
1 cup thinly sliced green onion (green portion and some of white portion)	1½ tablespoons sugar
	1¾ cups grated Cheddar cheese
1 10-ounce package frozen peas, thawed with cold water and drained	8 strips bacon, cooked, drained, and crumbled

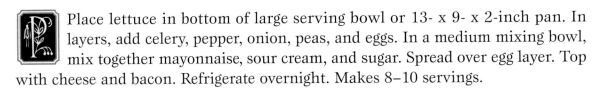 Place lettuce in bottom of large serving bowl or 13- x 9- x 2-inch pan. In layers, add celery, pepper, onion, peas, and eggs. In a medium mixing bowl, mix together mayonnaise, sour cream, and sugar. Spread over egg layer. Top with cheese and bacon. Refrigerate overnight. Makes 8–10 servings.

WALDORF CHICKEN SALAD

1   pound chicken breast
¾   cup mayonnaise
2   tablespoons honey
1   tablespoon cider vinegar
½   cup chopped celery
3   apples, chopped
½   cup walnuts, chopped
½   cup raisins

 Grill or bake the chicken until done; chill. Finely chop chicken and set aside. In a large bowl, stir together mayonnaise, honey, and vinegar. Add chicken, celery, apples, walnuts, and raisins; toss well to coat. Makes 4 servings.

LEMON PUDDING CAKE

¾   cup sugar
¼   cup all-purpose flour
⅛   teaspoon salt
3   tablespoons butter, melted
1½ teaspoons finely shredded lemon peel
¼   cup lemon juice
3   eggs, separated
1½ cup milk

Preheat oven to 350°F. In a large mixing bowl, combine sugar, flour, and salt. Stir in butter, lemon peel, and lemon juice. In a small bowl, beat egg yolks and pour in milk, mixing well; add to flour mixture. In a mixer bowl, beat egg whites to stiff peaks. Gently fold egg whites into lemon batter. Turn into an ungreased 8- x 8- x 2-inch baking pan. Place in a larger pan on oven rack. Pour hot water into larger pan to a depth of 1 inch. Bake 35 to 40 minutes or until top is golden and springs back when touched. Serve warm or chilled in individual dessert dishes. Makes 6–8 servings.

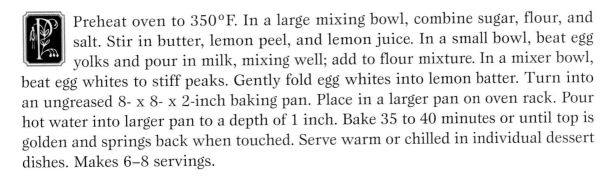

Delicious refreshments for a midday gathering, shared at home with friends and family

EIGHTY-EIGHT

The Quilting Bee

NADINE BROTHERS LYBARGER

Their hearts were all in rhythm
With their fingers and their stitching
As they sewed the small, straight stitches
That made Grandma's quilts bewitching.
They chatted and they tittered
As they lunched on cake and tea—
The sweet, old-fashioned ladies
At the hometown quilting bee.

Prim in fresh-starched cotton
As they labored in a row
On quilts of intricate design
With pieces set "just so."
Their skillful fingers wove a spell
Of stitches laid with care,
To make a masterpiece to show
At many a county fair.

"Friendship" quilts and "Wedding Rings,"
Just to name a few;
Sunburst patterns, bright and gay,
Old-fashioned "Nine-Patch" too;
"Rainbow" quilts and "Flower Pots"
In hand-sewn appliqué—
They never dreamed of machine-made quilts
Back in Grandma's day.

So here's to lovely ladies
And the fine heirlooms they made
While exchanging bits of gossip
At the local Ladies' Aid.
The art they plied was priceless
With their stitches—one, two, three—
The dedicated ladies
At the hometown quilting bee.

Gatherings at Home

A Party at Grandma's

Laura Ingalls Wilder

People had begun to come. They were coming on foot through the snowy woods, with their lanterns, and they were driving up to the door in sleds and wagons. Sleigh bells were jingling all the time.

The big room filled with tall boots and swishing skirts, and ever so many babies were lying in rows on Grandma's bed. Then Pa took his fiddle out of its box and began to play, and all the couples stood in squares on the floor and began to dance when Pa called the figures.

"Grand right and left!" Pa called out, and all the skirts began to swirl and all the boots began to stamp.

"Swing your partners!" Pa called, and "Each gent bow to the lady on your left!"

They all did as Pa said. Laura watched Ma's skirt swaying and her little waist bending and her dark head bowing, and she thought Ma was the loveliest dancer in the world.

The little circles and the big circles went round and round, and the skirts swirled and the boots stamped, and partners bowed and separated and met and bowed again.

In the kitchen Grandma was all by herself, stirring the boiling syrup on the big brass kettle. She stirred in time to the music. By the back door was a pail of clean snow, and sometimes Grandma took a spoonful of syrup from the kettle and poured it on some of the snow in a saucer.

Laura watched the dancers again. Pa was playing "The Irish Washerwoman" now. He called:

> Do-si, ladies, do-si-do,
> Come down heavy on your heel and toe!

Laura could not keep her feet still. Uncle George looked at her and laughed. Then he caught her by the hand and did a little dance with her, in the corner. She liked Uncle George.

Everybody was laughing, over by the kitchen door. They were dragging Grandma in from the kitchen. Grandma's dress was beautiful

Gatherings at Home

NINETY-TWO

too—a dark blue calico with autumn-colored leaves scattered over it. Her cheeks were pink from laughing, and she was shaking her head. The wooden spoon was in her hand.

"I can't leave the syrup," she said.

But Pa began to play "The Arkansas Traveler," and everybody began to clap in time to the music. So Grandma bowed to them all and did a few steps by herself. She could dance as prettily as any of them. The clapping almost drowned the music of Pa's fiddle.

Suddenly Uncle George did a pigeon wing, and bowing low before Grandma he began to jig. Grandma tossed her spoon to somebody. She put her hands on her hips and faced Uncle George, and everybody shouted. Grandma was jigging.

Laura clapped her hands in time to the music, with all the other clapping hands. The fiddle sang as it had never sung before. Grandma's eyes were snapping and her cheeks were red, and underneath her skirts her heels were clicking as fast as the thumping of Uncle George's boots.

Everybody was excited. Uncle George kept on jigging and Grandma kept on facing him, jigging too. The fiddle did not stop. Uncle George began to breathe loudly, and he wiped sweat off his forehead. Grandma's eyes twinkled.

"You can't beat her, George!" somebody shouted.

Uncle George jigged faster. He jigged twice as fast as he had been jigging. So did Grandma. Everybody cheered again. All the women were laughing and clapping their hands, and all the men were teasing George. George did not care, but he did not have breath enough to laugh. He was jigging.

Pa's blue eyes were snapping and sparking. He was standing up, watching George and Grandma, and the bow danced over the fiddle strings. Laura jumped up and down and squealed and clapped her hands.

Grandma kept on jigging. Her hands were on her hips and her chin was up and she was smiling. George kept on jigging, but his boots did not thump as loudly as they had thumped at first. Grandma's heels kept on clickety-clacking gaily. A drop of sweat dripped off George's forehead and shone on his cheek.

All at once he threw up both his arms and gasped, "I'm beat!" He stopped jigging.

Everybody made a terrific noise, shouting and yelling and stamping, cheering Grandma. Grandma jigged just a little minute more, then she stopped. She laughed in gasps. Her eyes sparkled just like Pa's when he laughed. George was laughing

All the women were laughing and clapping their hands, and all the men were teasing George.

too, and wiping his forehead on his sleeve.

Suddenly Grandma stopped laughing. She turned and ran as fast as she could into the kitchen. The fiddle had stopped playing. All the women were talking at once and all the men teasing George, but everybody was still for a minute, when Grandma looked like that.

Then she came to the door between the kitchen and the big room, and said, "The syrup is waxing. Come and help yourselves."

Then everybody began to talk and laugh again. They all hurried to the kitchen for plates, and outdoors to fill the plates with snow.

Grandma stood by the brass kettle, and with the big wooden spoon she poured hot syrup on each plate of snow. It cooled into soft candy, and as fast as it cooled they ate it.

They could eat all they wanted, for maple sugar never hurt anybody. There was plenty of syrup in the kettle, and plenty of snow outdoors. As soon as they ate one plateful, they filled their plates with snow again, and Grandma poured more syrup on it.

When they had eaten the soft maple candy until they could eat no more of it, then they helped themselves from the long table loaded with pumpkin pies and dried berry pies and cookies and cakes. There was salt-rising bread too, and cold boiled pork and pickles. Oh, how sour the pickles were!

They all ate till they could hold no more, and then they began to dance again. The room was loud and merry with the music of the fiddle and the noise of the dancing. The dancing was so pretty and the music so gay that Laura knew she would never get tired of it.

Gatherings at Home

Put on Your Old Gray Bonnet

STANLEY MURPHY

PERCY WENRICH

On the old farm-house ve - ran-da there sat Si - las and Mi - ran-da, think-ing of the days gone by. Said he, "Dear - ie, don't be wea - ry; you were al - ways bright and cheer-y, but a tear, dear, dims your eye." Said she, "They're tears of glad-ness, Si - las, they're not tears of sad-ness; it is fif - ty years to - day since we were wed."

Then the old man's dim eyes bright-en'd and his stern old heart, it light-en'd, as he

turned to her and said,_____ "Put on your old gray

bon - net with the blue rib - bon on it, while I hitch old

Dob - bin to the shay._____ And through the fields of

clo - ver, we'll drive up to Do - ver on our gold - en Wed - ding day."_____

Coffee Break

ELSIE ELAINE HALSEY

Oh, the coffee now is perking,
And the table's set for two;
There's coffee cake, if you want some,
And a coffee cup of blue.

A checkered cloth is on the table,
And the silverware's agleam.
There's a blue bowl of sugar
And a pitcher full of cream.

The curtains at the window
With their ruffled tiebacks, gay,
Send out an invitation,
So please don't stay away.

Geraniums, too, are blooming
Upon the windowsill.
Come and visit with me, neighbor,
And your coffee cup I'll fill.

There's a lot of friendship waiting.
The latchstring's out to you.
We'll chat awhile and laugh awhile.
That's exactly what we'll do.

So walk across the backyard
And click the garden gate.
I'm ready for my coffee break;
But if you'll come, I'll wait.

The ornaments of our house are the
friends who frequent it.
—RALPH WALDO EMERSON

Gatherings at Home

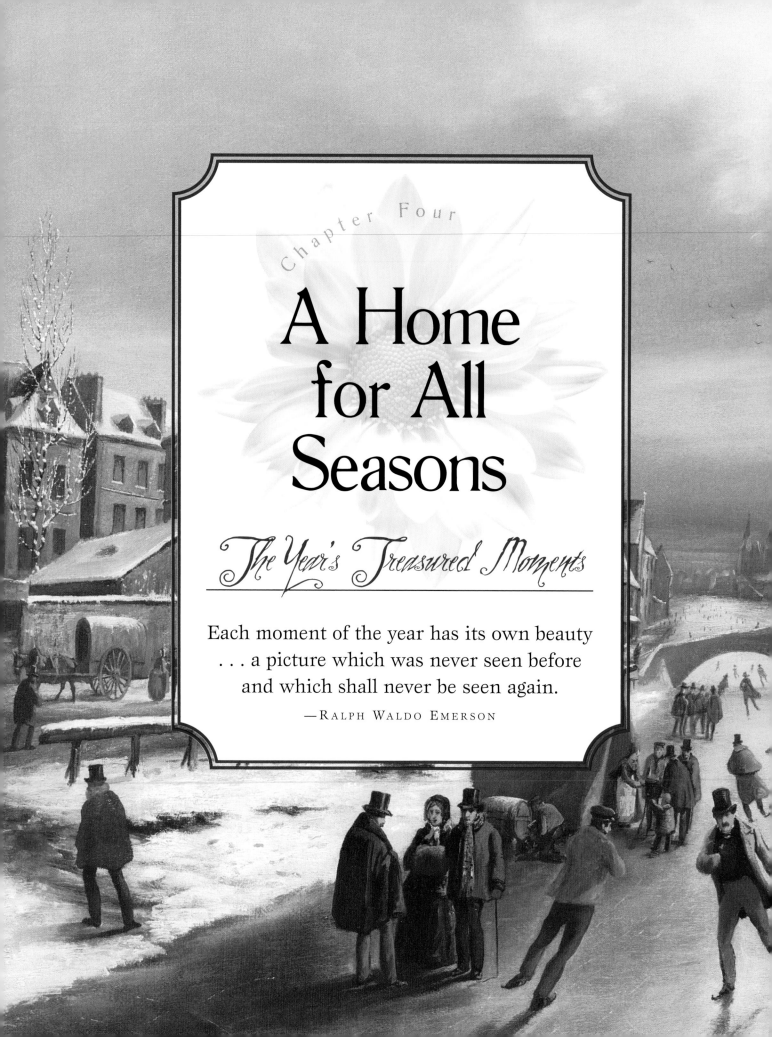

Chapter Four

A Home for All Seasons

The Year's Treasured Moments

Each moment of the year has its own beauty
. . . a picture which was never seen before
and which shall never be seen again.

—RALPH WALDO EMERSON

Colored Eggs and Jelly Beans

Bea Bourgeois

My husband, Bob, was the youngest of ten children born to Comb and Anna Anderson Bourgeois. Bob's memories of his childhood in northern Wisconsin remain vivid. When he talks about those distant days, the memories come alive; they are echoes of a way of life that has all but disappeared from the American scene.

Some of my older brothers and sisters had married and left home, and others were working in Ashland or Washburn. It was fun to have everybody back home for Easter dinner—our first reunion since Christmas. Ma and the girls always turned out a feast—sometimes roast chicken, a special treat in those days, or maybe a venison roast that came from the deer Pa had hunted the previous fall. Ma served her homemade chokecherry jelly and all kinds of home-canned pickles and relishes—even pickled eggs in beet juice. We had an Easter cake for dessert, which Ma decorated to look like a rabbit by snipping marshmallows for the ears and nose.

As poor as we were, Ma always produced Easter baskets full of treats for the children. She would make the "baskets" out of Mother's Oats boxes and cover them with yellow or green construction paper. There was no such thing as colored plastic grass, so Ma used a handful of hay as a nest for our candy and cookies.

She made fudge and divinity, and we each got some maple sugar candy. Ma baked sugar cookies in chicken and rabbit shapes, too, but the biggest surprise was always "boughten" jelly beans, which I still love, and those brightly colored candy eggs with soft marshmallow centers.

If we happened to have brown eggs (those were no good for coloring), we'd trade them for some white ones. We used food coloring and onion skins, and once in a while Ma and Dad would buy packaged dyes to color the eggs.

Home Sweet Home

Each basket had some of those furry little yellow chicks nestled in it too, and I used to get upset if the chicken happened to stick to one of my pieces of candy. We each got one of those delicate pastel papier-mâché rabbits or chickens that came from the dime store in town. I loved them because they had a pocket that was filled with jelly beans, and when I had eaten all the candy, I kept them on top of my dresser for decoration. Now they're collector's items!

As a child, I really believed the Easter Bunny worked late at night to get our baskets ready and then hide them in the strangest places around the house. One year I found mine in Ma's washing machine, and I thought that bunny was pretty clever.

We had a lot of good times hunting for colored eggs too. Some of them were in the usual places—behind the flour sack in the pantry, or under the couch in the living room. I remember one year when Milt and I were tearing through the house on our hunt, and we discovered a beautiful purple egg in the drawer of Ma's old foot-treadle sewing machine, behind the spools of thread and the bobbins.

There was no such thing as an Easter "parade" when I was growing up. First of all, it was much too cold for light spring clothing; we wore our heavy winter jackets to church.

ONE HUNDRED FOUR

And secondly, nobody ever got new clothes just because it was Easter. My sister Agnes remembers that the girls in the family got new dresses three times a year: when school started, at Christmas, and when school ended.

Because I was the youngest, I had to wear everybody else's hand-me-downs. If Ted, Frank, Ed, and Milt were done with it, I inherited it. I used to look through the Montgomery Ward catalog and wonder what it would be like to have a brand-new suit that had never belonged to anyone else!

When we "paraded" to church on Easter Sunday, I would inevitably be wearing a pair of Milt's pants and a coat that had belonged to Ed—tailored over to fit me, of course, but a "secondhand rose" just the same.

Spring Journey

RUTH B. FIELD

In the springtime we hitched up good old Nell;
And Gram and I rode away to town
With a clip-clop through the sweet spring smell
To buy a new hat and maybe a gown

With a guimpe and a sash, and some squeaky shoes.
Like tassels the catkins hung in the sun.
In town we would hear the latest news
And visit the notion store—what fun!

Penny dolls, candy in jars, bright beads,
Mustache cups, calico, crockery ware—
Here we could satisfy all our needs—
Ah, lovely the time that we spent there.

Burnished with joy were those sunny hours
Spent on a happy springtime ride—
Ring on a candy stick and flowers
On a hat as bright as the countryside.

Back over the road when the sun went down,
With precious bundles—life was a sonnet
To spring and a buggy ride to town
And a dream come true, my beflowered bonnet.

A Home for All Seasons

THE PETERKINS CELEBRATE THE FOURTH OF JULY

LUCRETIA P. HALE

In consideration of the fact that they had had no real celebration of the Fourth the last year, Mrs. Peterkin had consented to give over the day, this year, to the amusement of the family as a Centennial celebration. She would prepare herself for a terrible noise—only she did not want any gunpowder brought into the house.

The little boys had begun by firing some torpedoes a few days beforehand, that their mother might be used to the sound, and had selected their horns some weeks before.

Solomon John had been very busy in inventing some fireworks. As Mrs. Peterkin objected to the use of gunpowder, he found out from the dictionary what the different parts of gunpowder are—saltpeter, charcoal, and sulfur. Charcoal, he discovered, they had in the wood-house; saltpeter they would find in the cellar, in the beef barrel; and sulfur they could buy at the apothecary's. He explained to his mother that these materials had never yet exploded in the house, and she was quieted.

Agamemnon, meanwhile, remembered a recipe he had read somewhere for making a "fulminating paste" of iron filings and powder of brimstone. He had written it down on a piece of paper in his pocketbook. But the iron filings must be finely powdered. This they began upon a day or two before, and the very afternoon before laid out some of the paste on the piazza.

Pinwheels and rockets were contributed by Mr. Peterkin for the evening.

***

They sang patriotic songs, they told stories, they fired torpedoes, and they frightened the cats with them. It was a warm afternoon; the red poppies were out wide, and the hot sun poured down on the alleyways in the garden. There was a seething sound of a hot day in the buzzing of insects, in

the steaming heat that came up from the ground. Some neighboring boys were firing a toy cannon. Every time it went off Mrs. Peterkin started, and looked to see if one of the little boys was gone.

She asked Ann Maria if she were not anxious about the fireworks, and if rockets were not dangerous. They went up, but you were never sure where they came down.

And then came a fresh tumult! All the fire engines in town rushed toward them, clanging with bells, men and boys yelling! They were out for a practice and a Fourth of July show.

Mrs. Peterkin thought the house was on fire, and so did some of the guests.

There was great rushing hither and thither. Some thought they would better go home; some thought they would better stay. Mrs. Peterkin hastened into the house to save herself, or see what she could save. Elizabeth Eliza followed her, first proceeding to collect all the pokers and tongs she could find, because they could be thrown out of the window without breaking. She had read of people who had flung looking-glasses out of the window by mistake, in the excitement of the

house being on fire, and had carried the pokers and tongs carefully into the garden. There was nothing like being prepared. She had always determined to do the reverse. So with calmness she told Solomon John to take down the looking-glasses. But she met with a difficulty—there were no pokers and tongs, as they did not use them. They had no open fires; Mrs. Peterkin had been afraid of them. So Elizabeth Eliza took all the pots and kettles up to the upper windows, ready to be thrown out.

But where was Mrs. Peterkin? Solomon John found she had fled to the attic in terror.

He persuaded her to come down, assuring her it was the most unsafe place; but she insisted upon stopping to collect some bags of old pieces, which nobody would think of saving from the general wreck, she said, unless she did. Alas! This was the result of fireworks on the Fourth of July! As they came downstairs they heard the voices of all the company declaring there was no fire; the danger was past. It was long before Mrs. Peterkin could believe it. They told her the fire company was only out for show, and to celebrate the Fourth of July. She thought it already too much celebrated.

One Hundred Ten

Elizabeth Eliza's kettles and pans had come down through the windows with a crash; that had only added to the festivities, the little boys thought.

Torpedoes and crackers were fired at every pause. Some sweet-marjoram pots, tin cans filled with crackers which were lighted, went off with great explosions.

At the most exciting moment, Agamemnon, with an expression of terror, pulled Solomon John aside.

"I have suddenly remembered where I read about the 'fulminating paste' we made. It was in the preface to *Woodstock*, and I have been round to borrow the book to read the directions over again, because I was afraid about the 'paste' going off. Read this quickly! and tell me, *Where is the fulminating paste?*"

Solomon John was busy winding some covers of paper over a little parcel. It contained chlorate of potash and sulfur mixed. A friend had told him of the composition. The more thicknesses of paper you put round it, the louder it would go off. You must pound it with a hammer. Solomon John felt it must be perfectly safe, as his mother had taken potash for a medicine.

He still held the parcel as he read from Agamemnon's book: "This paste, when it has lain together about twenty-six hours, will *of itself* take fire, and burn all the sulfur away with a blue flame and a bad smell."

"Where is the paste?" repeated Solomon John, in terror.

"We made it just twenty-six hours ago," said Agamemnon.

"We put it on the piazza," exclaimed Solomon John, rapidly recalling the facts, "and it is in front of our mother's feet!"

A Home for All Seasons

He hastened to snatch the paste away before it should take fire, flinging aside the packet in his hurry. Agamemnon, jumping upon the piazza at the same moment, trod upon the paper parcel, which exploded at once with the shock, and he fell to the ground, while at the same moment the paste "fulminated" into a blue flame directly in front of Mrs. Peterkin!

It was a moment of great confusion. There were cries and screams. The bells were still ringing, the cannon firing.

"We are all blown up, as I feared we should be," Mrs. Peterkin at length ventured to say, finding herself in a lilac bush by the side of the piazza. She scarcely dared to open her eyes to see the scattered limbs about her.

It was so with all. Even Ann Maria Bromwick clutched a pillar of the piazza, with closed eyes.

At length Mr. Peterkin said, calmly, "Is anybody killed?"

Mrs. Peterkin was extricated from the lilac bush. No one knew how she got there.

There was no reply. Nobody could tell whether it was because everybody was killed, or because they were too wounded to answer. It was a great while before Mrs. Peterkin ventured to move.

But the little boys soon shouted with joy, and cheered the success of Solomon John's fireworks, and hoped he had some more. One of them had his face blackened by an unexpected cracker, and Elizabeth Eliza's muslin dress was burned here and there. But no one was hurt; no one had lost any limbs, though Mrs. Peterkin was sure she had seen some flying in the air. Nobody could understand how, as she had kept her eyes firmly shut.

No greater accident had occurred than the singeing of the tip of Solomon John's nose. But there was an unpleasant and terrible odor from the "fulminating paste."

Mrs. Peterkin was extricated from the lilac bush. No one knew how she got there.

Indeed, the thundering noise had stunned everybody. It had roused the neighborhood even more than before. Answering explosions came on every side, and, though the sunset light had not faded away, the little boys hastened to send off rockets under cover of the confusion. Solomon John's other fireworks would not go. But all felt he had done enough.

Mrs. Peterkin retreated into the parlor, deciding she had a headache. At times she had to come out when a rocket went off, to see if it was one of the little boys. She was exhausted by the adventures of the day, and almost thought it could not have been worse if the boys had been allowed gunpowder. The distracted lady was thankful there was likely to be but one Centennial Fourth in her lifetime, and declared she should never more keep anything in the house as dangerous as salt-petered beef, and she should never venture to take another spoonful of potash.

A Father to His Flag

D. A. HOOVER

"I pledge allegiance to the flag,"
I heard my father say,
And saw how proudly he beheld
Our colors on that day.

It was the "Fourth"—firecrackers popped,
Bands played, and clowns made noise—
A fun, exciting kind of day
For little girls and boys.

Then everybody was so still;
Old Glory marched on by.
I know I saw a tear of pride
Shine in my father's eye.

And then he smiled and said to me,
"My boy, of all you do,
Don't once forget this glorious sight,
Our own red, white, and blue!"

A Home for All Seasons

ONE HUNDRED FOURTEEN

Sounds of Thanksgiving

P. F. FREEMAN

It's nice to ride o'er familiar roads
And hear the sleigh bells ring,
To enjoy the many, many blessings
A Thanksgiving has to bring.
There is so much to be thankful for—
Joy seems to have no bounds;
It is a pleasure just to know
Thanksgiving Day has rolled around.

Memories soon are brought to mind
As kinfolks gather by the fireside—
There are many things to talk about
Which fleeting time could never hide.
While the snow in silence falls
To the cold and barren ground,
Frosty windows are a reminder that
Thanksgiving Day has rolled around.

The dining-room table has been spread,
There is food in every dish—
Turkey, potatoes, red cranberry jelly,
And whatever else you wish.
A rattling of dishes in the kitchen
Is to all a welcome sound,
For it means that once again
Thanksgiving Day has rolled around.

There is laughter, there is song,
And there's happiness everywhere,
While from the hills and mountaintops,
Winds of autumn glad tidings bear.
'Tis the season when loved ones mingle
To feast, to pray, and thanks propound,
For kindred folks are joyful that
Thanksgiving Day has rolled around.

A Home for All Seasons

AN OLD-FASHIONED THANKSGIVING

LOUISA MAY ALCOTT

Sixty years ago, up among the New Hampshire hills, lived Farmer Bassett, with a houseful of sturdy sons and daughters growing up about him. They were poor in money, but rich in land and love, for the wide acres of wood, corn, and pasture land fed, warmed, and clothed the flock, while mutual patience, affection, and courage made the old farmhouse a very happy home.

November had come; the crops were in, and barn, buttery, and bin were overflowing with the harvest that rewarded the summer's hard work. The big kitchen was a jolly place just now, for in the great fireplace roared a cheerful fire; on the walls hung garlands of dried apples, onions, and corn; up aloft from the beams shone crook-necked squashes, juicy hams, and dried venison—for in those days deer still haunted the deep forests, and hunters flourished. Savory smells were in the air; on the crane hung steaming kettles, and down among the red embers copper saucepans simmered, all suggestive of some approaching feast.

"Come, girls, fly round and get your chores done, so we can clear away for dinner jest as soon as I clap my bread into the oven," called Mrs. Bassett presently, as she rounded off the last loaf of brown bread which was to feed the hungry mouths that seldom tasted any other.

"Here's a man comin' up the hill lively!" "Guess it's Gad Hopkins. Pa told him to bring a dezzen oranges, if they warn't too high!" shouted Sol and Seth, running to the door, while the girls smacked their lips at the thought of this rare treat, and Baby threw his apple overboard, as if getting ready for a new cargo.

But all were doomed to disappointment, for it was not Gad, with the much-desired fruit. It was a stranger, who threw himself off his horse and hurried up to Mr. Bassett in the yard, with some brief message that made the farmer drop his ax and look so sober that his wife guessed at

A Home for All Seasons

once some bad news had come. And crying, "Mother's worse! I know she is!" out ran the good woman, forgetful of the flour on her arms and the oven waiting for its most important batch.

The man said old Mr. Chadwick, down at Keene, stopped him as he passed, and told him to tell Mrs. Bassett her mother was failin' fast, and she'd better come today. He knew no more; and having delivered his errand, he rode away, saying it looked like snow and he must be jogging, or he wouldn't get home till night.

"We must go right off, Eldad. Hitch up, and I'll be ready in less'n no time," said Mrs. Bassett, wasting not a minute in tears and lamentations, but pulling off her apron as she went in, with her head in a sad jumble of bread, anxiety, turkey, sorrow, haste, and cider applesauce.

* * *

At sunset the boys went out to feed the cattle, bring in heaps of wood, and lock up for the night, as the lonely farmhouse seldom had visitors after dark. The girls got the simple supper of brown bread and milk, baked apples, and a doughnut all round as a treat. Then they sat before the fire, the sisters knitting, the brothers with books or games, for Eph loved reading, and Sol and Seth never failed to play a few games of Morris with barley corns, on the little board they had themselves at one corner of the dresser.

When the moon-faced clock behind the door struck nine, Tilly tucked up the children under the "extry cornfortables," and, having kissed them all around, as Mother did, crept into her own nest, never minding the little drifts of snow that sifted in upon her coverlet between the shingles of the roof, nor the storm that raged without.

* * *

When they woke, like early birds, it still snowed, but up the little Bassetts jumped, broke the ice in their jugs, and went down with cheeks glowing like winter apples, after a brisk scrub and scramble into their clothes. Eph was off to the barn, and Tilly soon had a great kettle of mush ready, which with milk warm from the cows made a wholesome breakfast for the seven hearty children.

"Now about dinner," said the young housekeeper, as the pewter spoons stopped clattering, and the earthen bowls stood empty.

"Ma said, have what we liked, but she didn't expect us to have a real dinner together, because she won't be here to cook it, and we don't know how," began Prue, doubtfully.

"I can roast a turkey and make a pudding as well as anybody, I guess. The pies are all ready, and if we can't boil vegetables and so on, we don't deserve any dinner," cried Tilly, burning to distinguish herself, and bound to enjoy to the utmost her brief authority.

"Yes, yes!" cried all the boys, "Let's have a dinner anyway; Ma won't care, and the good victuals will spoil if they ain't eaten right up."

"Pa is coming tonight, so we won't have dinner till late; that will be real genteel and give us plenty of time," added Tilly, suddenly realizing the novelty of the task she had undertaken. "Now, sister, we'll have dinner at five; Pa will be here by that time, if he is coming tonight, and be so surprised to find us all ready, for he won't have had any very nice victuals if Gran'ma is so sick," she said, importantly. "I shall give the children a piece at noon" (Tilly meant luncheon); "doughnuts and cheese, with apple pie and cider, will please 'em. There's beans for Eph; he likes cold pork, so we won't stop to warm it up, for there's lots to do, and I don't mind saying to you I'm dreadful dubersome about the turkey."

"It's all ready but the stuffing, and roasting is as easy as can be. I can baste first-rate. Ma always likes to have me, I'm so patient and stiddy, she says," answered Prue. The responsibility of this great undertaking did not rest upon her, so she took a cheerful view of things.

"Now about dinner," said the young housekeeper, as the pewter spoons stopped clattering, and the earthen bowls stood empty.

ONE HUNDRED TWENTY

"Well, I'll get the puddin' off my mind fust, for it ought to bile all day. Put the big kettle on, and see that the spit is clean, while I get ready."

Prue obediently tugged away at the crane, with its black hooks, from which hung the iron teakettle and three-legged pot. Then she settled the long spit in the grooves made for it in the tall andirons and put the dripping pan underneath, for in those days meat was roasted as it should be, not baked in ovens.

Meantime Tilly attacked the plum pudding. She felt pretty sure of coming out right, here, for she had seen her mother do it so many times; it looked very easy. So in went suet and fruit; all sorts of spice, to be sure she got the right ones; and brandy instead of wine. But she forgot both sugar and salt, and tied it in the cloth so tightly that it had no room to swell, so it would come out as heavy as lead and as hard as a cannonball, if the bag did not burst and spoil it all. Happily unconscious of these mistakes, Tilly popped it into the pot, and proudly watched it bobbing about before she put the cover on and left it to its fate.

It took a long time to get all the vegetables ready, for, as the cellar was full, the girls thought they would have every sort. Eph helped, and by noon all was ready for cooking, and the cranberry sauce, a good deal scorched, was cooking in the lean-to.

"Now you all go and coast, while Prue and I set the table and get out the best chiny," said Tilly, bent on having her dinner look good, no matter what its other failings might be.

Eph took his fiddle and scraped away to his heart's content in the parlor, while the girls, after a short rest, set the table and made all ready to dish up the dinner when that exciting moment came. It was not at all the sort of table we see now, but would look very plain and countrified to us, with its green-handled knives and two-pronged steel forks, its red-and-white china and pewter platters, scoured till they shone, with mugs and spoons to match, and a brown jug for

Eph took his fiddle and scraped away to his heart's content in the parlor.

the cider. They had no napkins and little silver; but the best tankard and Ma's few wedding spoons were set forth in state. Nuts and apples at the corners gave an air, and the place of honor was left in the middle for the oranges yet to come.

"Don't it look beautiful?" said Prue, when they paused to admire the general effect.

***

They were just struggling to get the pudding out of the cloth when Roxy called out: "Here's Pa!"

"There's folks with him," added Rhody.

"Lots of 'em! I see two big sleighs chock-full," shouted Seth, peering through the dusk.

"I see Aunt Cinthy, and Cousin Hetty—and there's Mose and Amos. I do declare, Pa's bringin' 'em all home to have some fun here," cried Prue, as she recognized one familiar face after another.

"Oh, my patience! Ain't I glad I got dinner, and don't I hope it will turn out good!" exclaimed Tilly, while the twins pranced with delight, and the small boys roared: "Hooray for Pa! Hooray for Thanksgivin'!"

The cheer was answered heartily, and in came Father, Mother, Baby, aunts, and cousins, all in great spirits and all much surprised to find such a festive welcome awaiting them.

"Ain't Gran'ma dead at all?" asked Sol, in the midst of the kissing and handshaking.

"Bless your heart, no! It was all a mistake of old Mr. Chadwick's. He's as deaf as an adder, and when Mrs. Brooks told him Mother was mendin' fast, and she wanted me to come down today, certain sure, he got the message all wrong, and give it to the fust person passin' in such a way as to scare me 'most to death, and send us down in a hurry. Mother was sittin' up as chirk as you please, and dreadful sorry you didn't all come."

"So, to keep the house quiet for her, and give you a taste of the fun, your Pa fetched us all up to spend the evenin', and we are goin' to have a jolly time on't, to jedge by the looks of things," said Aunt Cinthy, briskly finishing the tale when Mrs. Bassett paused for want of breath.

"What in the world put it into your head we was comin', and set you to gittin' up such a supper?" asked Mr. Bassett, looking about him, well pleased and much surprised at the plentiful table.

Tilly modestly began to tell, but the others broke in and sang her praises in a sort of chorus, in which bears, pigs, pies, and oranges were oddly mixed. Great satisfaction was expressed by all, and Tilly and Prue were so elated by the commendation of Ma and the aunts, that they set forth their dinner, sure everything was perfect.

"I never see onions cooked better. All the vegetables is well done, and the dinner a credit to you, my dears," declared Aunt Cinthy, with her mouth full of the fragrant vegetable she praised.

The pudding was an utter failure in spite of the blazing brandy in which it lay—as hard and heavy as one of the stone balls on Squire Dunkin's great gate. It was speedily whisked out of sight, and all fell upon the pies, which were perfect. But Tilly and Prue were much depressed, and didn't recover their spirits till dinner was over and the evening fun well under way.

"Blind-man's bluff," "Hunt the slipper," "Come, Philander," and other lively games soon set everyone bubbling over with jollity, and when Eph struck up "Money Musk" on his fiddle, old and young fell into their places for a dance. All down the long kitchen they stood, Mr. and Mrs. Bassett at the top, the twins at the bottom, and then away they went, heeling and toeing, cutting pigeon-wings, and taking their steps in a way that would convulse modern children with their new-fangled romps called dancing.

Apples and cider, chat and singing, finished the evening, and after a grand kissing all round, the guests drove away in the clear moonlight which came out to cheer their long drive.

When the jingle of the last bell had died away, Mr. Bassett said soberly, as they stood together on the hearth: "Children,

ONE HUNDRED TWENTY-THREE

we have special cause to be thankful that the sorrow we expected was changed into joy, so we'll read a chapter 'fore we go to bed, and give thanks where thanks is due."

Then Tilly set out the light stand with the big Bible on it, and a candle on each side, and all sat quietly in the firelight, smiling as they listened with happy hearts to the sweet old words that fit all times and seasons so beautifully.

When the good-nights were over, and the children in bed, Prue put her arm round Tilly and whispered tenderly, for she felt her shake, and was sure she was crying:

"Don't mind about the old puddin', deary—nobody cared, and Ma said we really did do surprisin' well for such young girls."

The laughter Tilly was trying to smother broke out then, and was so infectious, Prue could not help joining her, even before she knew the cause of the merriment.

Here a smart rap on the wall of the next room caused a sudden lull in the fun, and Mrs. Bassett's voice was heard, saying warningly, "Girls, go to sleep immediate, or you'll wake the baby."

"Yes'm," answered two meek voices, and after a few irrepressible giggles, silence reigned, broken only by an occasional snore from the boys, or the soft scurry of mice in the buttery, taking their part in this old-fashioned Thanksgiving.

F.D.Hardy. 1891.

ONE HUNDRED TWENTY-FIVE

A Home for All Seasons

CORN AND WINTER SQUASH WITH SPINACH AND BACON

9 bacon slices, chopped
2 cups chopped onion
2½ pounds butternut squash, peeled, seeded, and cut into ⅓-inch pieces
9 ounces baby spinach leaves

1 16-ounce package frozen corn kernels, thawed
6 tablespoons chopped fresh basil
Salt
Pepper

In a large skillet, cook bacon over medium heat until crisp, about 10 minutes. Add onions and squash. Sauté until squash is almost tender, about 12 minutes. Add spinach and corn. Toss until spinach wilts and corn is heated through, about 5 minutes. Stir in basil. Season with salt and pepper. Transfer to bowl and serve. Makes 8 to 10 servings.

For the Holiday Table

SWEET POTATO AND APPLE DRESSING

1 8- to 10-ounce sweet potato, peeled and diced
2 tablespoons vegetable oil
½ cup chopped onion
½ cup diced red-skinned apple

⅓ cup chopped celery
1½ cups herb-seasoned stuffing mix
½ teaspoon rubbed dried sage
1 cup canned low-salt chicken broth

Preheat oven to 375°F. Cook sweet potato in small pot of boiling salted water until just tender, about 5 minutes. Drain and set aside. In heavy medium skillet, heat oil over medium heat. Add onion, apple, and celery; sauté until onion is translucent, abut 5 minutes. Add potato; sauté 1 minute. Stir in stuffing mix, sage, and broth. Cover skillet, reduce heat to medium-low and cook until stock is absorbed, about 10 minutes. Season to taste with salt and pepper. Transfer dressing to buttered 4-cup casserole dish. Cover with foil and bake until heated through, about 30 minutes. Uncover and bake until top begins to brown, about 15 minutes. Makes 4 servings.

GREAT-GRANDMOTHER'S CLOVERLEAF ROLLS

9 tablespoons unsalted butter, divided	1 ¼-ounce package (2¼ teaspoons) active dry yeast
¼ cup sugar	½ cup warm (110°F) water
1 teaspoon salt	1 large egg, beaten
¾ cup milk	3½ cups all-purpose flour

In a large bowl, mix 3 tablespoons butter with sugar and salt. In a small saucepan, heat the milk until warm; pour over the butter mixture and let cool. In a small bowl, sprinkle the yeast over the warm water; set aside to proof until foamy, about 5 minutes. Stir the yeast mixture into the butter mixture. Beat in the egg, then beat in the flour until you have a soft dough. Cover and refrigerate.

Two hours before baking, turn dough out onto a floured surface and divide it in half. Divide each half into 6 equal portions, then divide each portion into 3 pieces. Melt 6 tablespoons butter. Roll each piece of dough into a ball and dip in melted butter. Place in a muffin tin, 3 balls to a muffin cup. Cover with plastic wrap and let rise in a warm place until doubled in volume, about 1½ hours.

Preheat the oven to 350°F. Bake 15 minutes or until golden brown. Makes 1 dozen rolls.

MAPLE-PECAN PIE

1 cup maple syrup	1 tablespoon all-purpose flour
¾ cup golden brown sugar	1 teaspoon vanilla extract
3 large eggs	1 9-inch frozen deep-dish pie crust
¼ cup granulated sugar	1½ cups coarsely chopped pecans
3 tablespoons butter, melted	

Preheat oven to 350°F. In a medium bowl, whisk first 7 ingredients until blended. Place unbaked crust on baking sheet. Spread pecans in bottom of pie crust. Pour filling over pecans. Bake until filling is set and slightly puffed, about 1 hour. Transfer pie to rack and cool completely. Makes 8 servings.

Flavorful trimmings for seasonal celebrations in the home

A Home for All Seasons

Christmas at Grandma's

ERNEST JACK SHARPE

Hitch up the horses, climb in the sleigh;
Cover up warm, for we're off today
For a Christmas at Grandma's house,
For an old-fashioned Christmas like those long ago.

Sleigh bells are jingling as we jog along;
The crisp air is filled with laughter and song.
And soon we arrive and happily call,
"Merry Christmas! Merry Christmas! Merry Christmas to all."

The table is loaded with good things piled high.
And we stuff ourselves full with turkey and pie.
What a day! What a day! What presents! What fun!
And oh, are we tired, when the long day is done.

Tired, but happy, we fall into bed;
And soon, merry dreams come and dance through our head.
Such was a Christmas as we used to know,
A Christmas at Grandma's in days long ago.

By the fireside still the light is shining.
The children's arms round the parents twining.
From love so sweet, oh, who would roam?
Be it ever so homely, home is home.

—D. M. MULOCK

Home Sweet Home

A Home for All Seasons

The Spell of Silver Bells

HELEN WHITEMAN SHICK

Under the spell of silver bells,
Old pleasures of long ago
Come seeping out of memory's well
To brighten the Christmas glow.
The tinkly, silvery echo-chimes
Are melodies out of the past,
For they sing of childhood's happy times—
The wonderful joys that will last.

Under the spell of silver bells,
There's a tree all spangled and bright,
And carols the holiday joys foretell
Making laughter on Christmas night.

A great holly wreath at the window hangs,
And stockings are bulging too;
There's a heavenly scent of evergreen tang
And a firelight sparkling anew.

A big paper bell from the chandelier
Is hanging with mistletoe near it;
And candles are flickering mellowness
For a room full of Christmas spirit.
There's a home where a family of loved ones dwell
In the picture of long, long ago,
As memory quickens with silver bells
To brighten the Christmas glow.

The Christmas Tree in the Nursery

RICHARD WATSON GILDER

With wild surprise
Four great eyes
In two small heads
From neighboring beds
Looked out—and winked—
And glittered and blinked
At a very queer sight
In the dim dawn-light.
As plain as can be,
A fairy tree
Flashes and glimmers
And shakes and shimmers.
Red, green, and blue
Meet their view;
Silver and gold
Sharp eyes behold;
Small moons, big stars,
And jams in jars;
And cakes and honey,
And thimbles and money;

Pink dogs, blue cats,
Little squeaking rats,
And candles and dolls,
And crackers and polls,
A real bird that sings,
And tokens and favors,
And all sorts of things
For the little shavers.

Four black eyes
Grow big with surprise,
And then grow bigger
When a tiny figure,
Jaunty and airy,
A fairy! a fairy!
From the tree-top cries,
"Open wide! Black Eyes!
Come, children, wake now!
Your joys you may take now!"

Quick as you can think,
Twenty small toes
In four pretty rows,
Like little piggies pink,
All kick in the air—
And before you can wink,
The tree stands bare!

Let's dance and sing and make good cheer,
For Christmas comes but once a year.
—SIR GEORGE ALEXANDER MACFARREN

A Home for All Seasons

Remembering a Childhood Christmas

CHARLES DICKENS

I have been looking on, this evening, at a merry company of children assembled round that pretty German toy, a Christmas Tree. The tree was planted in the middle of a great round table, and towered high above their heads. It was brilliantly lighted by a multitude of little tapers, and everywhere sparkled and glittered with bright objects.

Being now at home again, and alone, the only person in the house awake, my thoughts are drawn back, by a fascination which I do not care to resist, to my own childhood. If I no more come home at Christmastime, there will be boys and girls (thank Heaven!) while the World lasts; and they do! Yonder they dance and play upon the branches of my Tree, God bless them, merrily, and my heart dances and plays too!

And I do come home at Christmas. We all do, or we all should. We all come home, or ought to come home, for a short holiday—the longer, the better—from the great boarding school, where we are for ever working at our arithmetical slates, to take, and give, a rest. As to going a-visiting, where can we not go, if we will; where have we not been, when we would; starting our fancy from our Christmas Tree!

Away into the winter prospect. There are many such upon the tree! On, by low-lying, misty grounds, through fens and fogs, up long hills, winding dark as caverns between thick plantations, almost shutting out the sparkling stars; so, out on broad heights, until we stop at last, with sudden silence, at an avenue. The gate-bell has a deep, half-awful sound in the frosty air; the gate swings open on its hinges; and, as we drive up to a great house, the glancing lights grow larger in the windows, and the opposing rows of trees seem to fall solemnly back on either side, to give us place. And so, the lights growing larger, and the trees falling back before us, and closing up again behind us, as if to forbid retreat, we come to the house.

Home Sweet Home

There is probably a smell of roasted chestnuts and other good comfortable things all the time, for we are telling Winter Stories—Ghost Stories, or more shame for us—round the Christmas fire; and we have never stirred, except to draw a little nearer to it. But, no matter for that. We came to the house, and it is an old house, full of great chimneys where wood is burnt on ancient logs upon the hearth.

Encircled by the social thoughts of Christmastime, still let the benignant figure of my childhood stand unchanged! In every cheerful image and suggestion that the season brings, may the bright star that rested above the poor roof be the star of all the Christian World! A moment's pause, O vanishing tree, of which the lower boughs are dark to me as yet, and let me look once more! If Age be hiding for me in the unseen portion of thy downward growth, oh, may I, with a grey head, turn a child's heart to that figure yet, and a child's trustfulness and confidence!

Now, the tree is decorated with bright merriment, and song, and dance, and cheerfulness. And they are welcome. Innocent and welcome be they ever held, beneath the branches of the Christmas Tree, which cast no gloomy shadow!

A Home for All Seasons

I'll Be Home for Christmas

Kim Gannon

Walter Kent

I'll   be   home   for   Christ - mas;_____

You   can   plan   on   me.   Please   have

snow   and   mis - tle - toe   And   pres - ents   on   the

tree._____ Christ - mas Eve will find me_____

Where the love - light gleams.

I'll be home for Christ - mas, If on - ly

in my dreams.   dreams.

Chapter Five

Memories of Home

A Place in the Heart

When the hornet hangs in the hollyhock,
And the brown bee drones i' the rose,
And the west is a red-streaked four-o'clock,
And summer is near its close,
It's—Oh, for the gate, and the locust lane;
And dusk, and dew, and home again!

—MADISON JULIUS CAWEIN

SMALL-TOWN HOME

BESS STREETER ALDRICH

Once a story of mine, syndicated in a newspaper, carried in brackets an indulgent explanation from an editor that the writer "goes right down into small towns and mingles among the people for her material." Could anything sound more smug? As if I had gone slumming with drawn skirts. I have not gone small-townish for material. I *am* small-townish.

Of course, to be honest, I admit I would not choose this little place if I were driving across country seeking a town into which to move. I may have expressed something of that in the introduction to *A Lantern in Her Hand*; for, while the Cedartown of the story is fictitious, it is frankly located in this section of the country.

"Cedartown sits beside a highway which was once a buffalo trail. If you start in one direction on the highway and travel far enough, you will come to the effete East. If you travel a few hundred miles farther in the opposite direction, you will come to the distinctive West. Cedartown is neither effete nor distinctive nor is it even particularly pleasing to passing tourists. It is beautiful only in the eyes of those who live here and in the memories of the Nebraska-born whose dwelling in far places has given them moments of home-sickness for the low rolling hills, the swell and dip of the ripening wheat, the fields of sinuously waving corn, and the elusively fragrant odor of alfalfa."

After all, it is contact and familiarity that help endear people and places to us. I came here in a happy day, and perhaps I am trying to cling to old happiness.

As I write, I have only to glance outside my study window to see in the cement of the driveway the tracings of a fat hand with grotesque square fingers, a date of nine years ago, and the straggling initials C.S.A. I have one son who has always had a perfect obsession for leaving his footprints, not only on the sands of time but in every piece of new cement about the place. There are hands and feet of every size, width, and length on sidewalks, driveways, steps, and posts, all duly signed and dated.

Home Sweet Home

It would be absurd to say that the sight of that traced hand outside my study window holds me here, but it may readily be a symbol of all that does. It would not be possible for me to follow four young people with widely diversified tastes and talents out into the world; and to keep the home with its old associations means more to me than any advantage gained by moving cityward.

This is the home my sons and daughter knew in childhood; and I have a notion that in this rather hectic day of complicated life, it is well for young people to have some substantial tie which still holds them to the anchor of unchanging things. You cannot break the radii which stretch out from the center of a good home. They are the most flexible things in the world. They reach out into every port where a child has strayed— these radii of love. They pull at the hearts of the children until sometime, somewhere, they draw the wanderers all back into the family circle.

Memories of Home

Grandma's House

BARBARA W. WEBER

It seems it was just yesterday—
    The rooms were strewn about with toys,
And all the house with laughter rang
    Of happy little girls and boys.

And all about were teddy bears
    And dolls and trikes and baby bibs,
And when each busy day was done,
    She tucked the toddlers in their cribs.

The children, as the years flew by,
    Became teenagers, strong and tall;
But strangely, on the other hand,
    The house seemed somehow to grow small.

Then, one by one, they went away
    Till all had flown, and none were there,
And suddenly, the house grew large;
    The rooms were empty, still, and bare.

But it must be as I've heard told,
    And I believe it's surely true,
That what you freely give away
    Returns abundantly to you.

Now when they all come visiting,
    The house once more is strewn with toys.
She smiles to hear the laughter of
    Her children's little girls and boys.

For Grandma's heart and home are kin:
    A welcome sign hangs on each door,
And no one's left outside, for there
    Is always room for yet one more.

Memories of Home

CHOCOLATE CHIP AND OATMEAL COOKIES

1 package (about 18 ounces) yellow cake mix
1 cup quick-cooking rolled oats

¾ cup butter, softened
2 eggs
1 cup semi-sweet chocolate chips

Preheat oven to 350°F. Combine cake mix, oats, butter, and eggs in large bowl; beat until well blended. Stir in chocolate chips. Drop by rounded teaspoons onto ungreased cookie sheet. Bake 10 to 12 minutes or until very lightly browned. Cool slightly on pan; remove from cookie sheet to wire rack and cool completely. Makes 4 dozen cookies.

PEANUT BUTTER COCONUT BARS

¾ cup unsalted butter, softened
1 cup granulated sugar
1 cup creamy peanut butter
1 large egg
1 teaspoon vanilla

½ teaspoon salt
2 cups all-purpose flour
2 cups sweetened flaked coconut
½ cup finely chopped salted, roasted peanuts

Preheat oven to 350°F. In a large mixing bowl, using an electric mixer, cream butter and sugar; beat until light and fluffy. Add peanut butter and beat until well combined; beat in egg, vanilla, and salt. Add flour; beat until just combined. Stir in coconut. Spread batter evenly in a buttered 15½- x 10½- x 1-inch jelly-roll pan. Sprinkle peanuts over batter and press them in lightly. Bake 20 to 25 minutes, or until a tester comes out clean. Let cool completely in pan on a rack. Cut into 24 rectangles, then cut each bar in half diagonally to form 2 triangles. Makes 4 dozen bars.

PRALINE SQUARES

¼ cup shortening
1 cup light brown sugar
1 egg
¾ cup all-purpose flour

1 teaspoon baking powder
½ teaspoon salt
½ teaspoon vanilla
½ cup chopped pecans

Preheat oven to 350°F. In a large saucepan, melt shortening over low heat. Remove from heat and blend in brown sugar; cool. Stir in egg. In a medium mixing bowl, mix flour, baking powder, and salt. Add flour mixture to shortening mixture; mix well. Stir in vanilla and pecans. Spread in a greased and floured 8- x 8 -x 2-inch pan. Bake 25 minutes, until a light touch with a finger leaves slight imprint. Cut into 2- x 1-inch bars while warm. Makes 18 bars.

APPLE-BUTTER REFRIGERATOR COOKIES

1 cup granulated sugar
1 cup butter, softened
¼ cup apple butter
1 egg
2½ cups all-purpose flour

1 cup finely shredded Cheddar
   cheese (4 ounces)
½ teaspoon baking soda
½ teaspoon apple pie spice

Mix sugar, butter, apple butter, and egg. Stir in remaining ingredients. Cover and refrigerate at least 2 hours.

Divide dough in half. Roll each half into a log about 1½ inches in diameter and 8 inches long. Wrap in waxed paper and refrigerate at least 4 hours.

Preheat oven to 400°F. Gently peel paper off of each log and cut log into ⅛-inch slices. Place about 1 inch apart on an ungreased cookie sheet. Bake 7 to 9 minutes or until edges are light brown; remove cookie sheet to rack and let stand until the cookies firm slightly. Transfer cookies to rack to cool. Makes 6 dozen cookies.

Sweet reminders of afternoons in a sunny kitchen with loved ones

One Hundred Forty-Four

Around the World with Dad

REGINALD HOLMES

I often sat upon his knee,
When I was just a lad,
For nightly trips of make-believe
Around the world with Dad.

We'd climb the Himalayas
To hunt the bighorn sheep
Or sail away to Africa
And jungles dark and deep.

We'd visit ancient castles
In Scotland's verdant vales
Or sail on expeditions
To look for sharks or whales.

We'd land on tropic islands
And live on fish and fruit
Or maybe hunt for treasure
Where pirates hid their loot.

We'd often sail with Kipling
To watch the dolphins play,
Explore the old pagodas
When we had crossed the bay.

We both had such a lot of fun
Until my mother said,
"Come on, you weary traveler,
It's time you were in bed."

But if I'd ever told my mom
What frightful dreams I had,
She never would have let me
Go around the world with Dad.

The Old Porch Swing

RUTH H. UNDERHILL

Something I miss on a house today
Is the old porch swing where we would sway.
When we were kids we'd sit in a row
And gently rock it to and fro.

This was our seat on a rainy day;
We would sit and watch the raindrops play.
We'd listen to the loud thunder roar
And watch the lightning streak and soar.

And then, upon a sunshine day,
We'd gather up our dolls to play.
And out they'd go to the old porch swing,
Our close haven from everything.

When baby brother would fret and cry,
Mother would rock him by and by.
His tiny head nestled near her chin;
She'd forward rock, then back again.

It seems like such an age ago
When gently we'd rock to and fro.
And then a sweet melody we'd sing
And gently sway in the old porch swing.

To most men their early home is
no more than a memory of their
early years. The image is never
marred. There's no disappointment
in memory, and one's exaggerations
are always on the good side.

—GEORGE ELIOT

Memories of Home

MOLE'S HOUSE

KENNETH GRAHAME

We others, who have long lost the more subtle of the
physical senses, have not even proper terms to express an animal's inter-
communications with his surroundings, living or otherwise, and have
only the word "smell," for instance, to include the whole range of delicate thrills which murmur in the nose of the animal night and day, sum-
moning, warning, inciting, repelling. It was one of these mysterious fairy
calls from out of the void that suddenly reached Mole in the darkness,
making him tingle through and through with its very familiar appeal,
even while yet he could not clearly remember what it was. He stopped
dead in his tracks, his nose searching hither and thither in its efforts to
recapture the fine filament, the telegraphic current, that had so strongly
moved him. A moment, and he had caught it again; and with it this time
came recollection in fullest flood.

Home! That was what they meant—those caressing appeals, those
soft touches wafted through the air, those invisible little hands pulling
and tugging, all one way! Why, it must be quite close by him at that
moment, his old home that he had hurriedly forsaken and never sought
again, that day when he first found the river! And now it was sending
out its scouts and its messengers to capture him and bring him in. Since
his escape on that bright morning, he had hardly given it a thought, so
absorbed had he been in his new life, in all its pleasures, its surprises, its
fresh and captivating experiences. Now, with a rush of old memories,
how clearly it stood up before him, in the darkness! Shabby indeed, and
small and poorly furnished, and yet his, the home he had made for himself, the home he had been so happy to get back to after his day's work.
And the home had been happy with him too, evidently, and was missing
him, and wanted him back, and was telling him so, through his nose—
sorrowfully, reproachfully, but with no bitterness or anger, only with
plaintive reminder that it was there, and wanted him.

The call was clear, the summons was plain. He must obey it instantly,

Home Sweet Home

ONE HUNDRED FORTY-SEVEN

and go. "Ratty!" he called, full of joyful excitement, "Hold on! Come back! I want you, quick!"

"Oh, come along, Mole, do!" replied the Rat cheerfully, still plodding along.

"Please stop, Ratty!" pleaded the poor Mole, in anguish of heart. "You don't understand! It's my home, my old home! I've just come across the smell of it, and it's close by here, really quite close. And I must go to it, I must, I must! Oh, come back, Ratty! Please, please come back!"

"Mole, we mustn't stop now, really!" he called back. "We'll come for it tomorrow, whatever it is you've found. But I daren't stop now—it's late, and the snow's coming on again, and I'm not sure of the way! And I want your nose, Mole, so come on quick, there's a good fellow!" And the Rat pressed forward on his way without waiting for an answer.

Poor Mole stood alone in the road, his

heart torn asunder, and a big sob gathering, gathering, somewhere low down inside him, to leap up to the surface presently, he knew, in passionate escape. But even under such a test as this, his loyalty to his friend stood firm. Never for a moment did he dream of abandoning him. Meanwhile, the wafts from his old home pleaded, whispered, conjured, and finally claimed him imperiously. With a wrench that tore his very heartstrings he set his face down the road and followed submissively in the track of the Rat; while faint, thin little smells, still dogging his retreating nose, reproached him for his new friendship and his callous forgetfulness.

With an effort he caught up to the unsuspecting Rat, who began chattering cheerfully about what they would do when they got back, and how jolly a fire of logs in the parlor would be, and what a supper he meant to eat; never noticing his companion's silence and distressful state of mind. At last, however, when they had gone some considerable way further, and were passing some tree stumps at the edge of a copse that bordered the road, he stopped and said kindly, "Look here, Mole old chap, you seem dead tired. No talk left in you, and your feet dragging like lead. We'll sit down here for a minute and rest. The snow has held off so far, and the best part of our journey is over."

The Mole subsided forlornly on a tree stump and tried to control himself, for he felt it surely coming. The sob he had fought with so long refused to be beaten. Up and up, it forced its way to the air, and then another, and another, and others

thick and fast, till poor Mole at last gave up the struggle and cried freely and helplessly and openly, now that he knew it was all over and he had lost what he could hardly be said to have found.

The Rat, astonished and dismayed at the violence of Mole's paroxysm of grief, did not dare to speak for a while. At last he said, very quietly and sympathetically, "What is it, old fellow? Whatever can be the matter? Tell us your trouble, and let me see what I can do."

Poor Mole found it difficult to get any words out between the upheavals of his chest that followed one upon another so quickly and held back speech and choked it as it came. "I know it's a—shabby, dingy little place," he sobbed forth at last, brokenly: "not like—your cozy quarters—or Toad's beautiful hall—or Badger's great house— but it was my own little home—and I was fond of it—and I went away and forgot all about it—and then I smelt it suddenly—on the road, when I called and you wouldn't listen, Rat—and everything came back to me with a rush—and I *wanted* it!—oh, dear, oh, dear!—and when you *wouldn't*

Meanwhile, the wafts from his old home pleaded, whispered, conjured, and finally claimed him imperiously.

turn back, Ratty—and I had to leave it, though I was smelling it all the time—I thought my heart would break. We might have just gone and had one look at it, Ratty—only one look—it was close by—

Memories of Home

ONE HUNDRED FIFTY

but you wouldn't turn back, Ratty, you wouldn't turn back! Oh, dear, oh, dear!"

Recollection brought fresh waves of sorrow, and sobs again took full charge of him, preventing further speech.

The Rat stared straight in front of him, saying nothing, only patting Mole gently on the shoulder. After a time he muttered gloomily, "I see it all now! What a *pig* I have been! A pig—that's me! Just a pig—a plain pig!"

He waited till Mole's sobs became gradually less stormy and more rhythmical; he waited till at last sniffs were frequent and sobs only intermittent. Then he rose from his seat and, remarking carelessly, "Well, now we'd really better be getting on, old chap!" set off up the road again, over the toilsome way they had come.

"Wherever are you (hic) going to (hic), Ratty?" cried the tearful Mole, looking up in alarm.

"We're going to find that home of yours, old fellow," replied the Rat pleasantly. "So you had better come along, for it will take some finding, and we shall want your nose."

Still snuffling, pleading, and reluctant, Mole suffered himself to be dragged back along the road by his imperious companion, who by a flow of cheerful talk and anecdote endeavored to beguile his spirits back and make the weary way seem shorter. When at last it seemed to the Rat that they must be nearing that part of the road where the Mole had been "held up," he said, "Now, no more talking. Business! Use your nose, and give your mind to it."

They moved on in silence for some little way, when suddenly the Rat was conscious, through his arm that was linked in Mole's, of a faint sort of electric thrill that was passing down that animal's body. Instantly he disengaged himself, fell back a pace, and waited, all attention.

The signals were coming through!

Mole stood a moment rigid, while his uplifted nose, quivering slightly, felt the air.

Mole stood a moment rigid, while his uplifted nose, quivering slightly, felt the air.

Suddenly, without giving warning, he dived; but the Rat was on the alert, and promptly followed him down the tunnel to which his unerring nose had faithfully led him.

The Mole struck a match, and by its light the Rat saw that they were standing in an open space, neatly swept and sanded underfoot, and directly facing them was Mole's little front door, with "Mole End" painted, in Gothic lettering, over the bell-pull at the side.

Mole reached down a lantern from a nail on the wall and lit it; and the Rat, looking round him, saw that they were in a sort of fore-court. Mole's face beamed at the sight of all these objects so dear to him, and he hurried Rat through the door, lit a lamp in the hall, and took one glance round his old home. He saw the dust lying thick on everything, saw the cheerless, deserted look of the long-neglected house, and its narrow, meager dimensions, its worn and shabby contents—and collapsed again on a hall chair, his nose to his paws. "Oh, Ratty!" he cried dismally, "Why ever did I do it? Why did I bring you to this poor, cold little place, on a night like this, when you might have been at River Bank by this time, toasting your toes before a blazing fire, with all your own nice things about you!"

The Rat paid no heed to his doleful self-reproaches. He was running here and there, opening doors, inspecting rooms and cupboards, and lighting lamps and candles and sticking them up everywhere. "What a capital little house this is!" he called out cheerily. "So compact! So well planned! Everything here and everything in its place! We'll make a jolly night of it. The first thing we want is a good fire; I'll see to

They went and foraged, hunting through every cupboard and turning out every drawer.

that—I always know where to find things. So this is the parlor? Splendid! Your own idea, those little sleeping-bunks in the wall? Capital! Now, I'll fetch the wood and the coals, and you get a duster, Mole— you'll find one in the drawer of the kitchen table—and try and smarten things up a bit. Bustle about, old chap!"

Encouraged by his inspiriting companion, the Mole roused himself and dusted and polished with energy and heartiness, while the Rat, running to and fro with armfuls of fuel, soon had a cheerful blaze roaring up the chimney. They went and foraged, hunting through every cupboard and turning out every drawer. The result was not so very depressing after all, though

of course it might have been better: a tin of sardines, a box of captain's biscuits, nearly full, and a German sausage encased in silver paper.

"There's a banquet for you!" observed the Rat, as he arranged the table. "I know some animals who would give their ears to be sitting down to supper with us tonight! This is really the jolliest little place I ever was in. Now, wherever did you pick up those prints? Make the place look so home-like, they do. No wonder you're so fond of it, Mole. Tell us all about it, and how you came to make it what it is."

Then, while the Rat busied himself fetching plates, and knives and forks, and mustard which he mixed in an egg cup, the Mole, his bosom still heaving with the stress of his recent emotion, related—somewhat shyly at first, but with more freedom as he warmed to his subject—how this was planned, and how that was thought out, and how this was got through a windfall from an aunt, and that was a wonderful find and a bargain, and this other thing was bought out of laborious savings and a certain amount of "going without."

In a very few minutes supper was ready, and Mole, as he took the head of the table in a sort of a dream, saw a lately barren board set thick with savory comforts; and then let himself loose—for he was famished indeed—on the provender so magically provided, thinking what a happy homecoming this had turned out, after all.

At last the Rat, with a tremendous yawn, said, "Mole, old chap, I'm ready to drop. Sleepy is simply not the word. That

your own bunk over on that side? Very well, then, I'll take this. What a ripping little house this is! Everything so handy!"

He clambered into his bunk and rolled himself well up in the blankets, and slumber gathered him forthwith, as a swathe of barley is folded into the arms of the reaping machine.

The weary Mole also was glad to turn in without delay, and soon had his head on his pillow, in great joy and contentment. But ere he closed his eyes he let them wander round his old room, mellow in the glow of the firelight that played or rested on familiar and friendly things which had long been unconsciously a part of him, and now smilingly received him back, without ran-

cor. He saw clearly how plain and simple—how narrow, even—it all was; but clearly, too, how much it all meant to him, and the special value of some such anchorage in one's existence. He did not at all want to abandon the new life and its splendid spaces, to turn his back on sun and air and all they offered him and creep home and stay there; the upper world was all too strong—it called to him still, even down there, and he knew he must return to the larger stage. But it was good to think he had this to come back to; this place which was all his own, these things which were so glad to see him again and could always be counted upon for the same simple welcome.

Memories of Home

HOME SWEET HOME

JOHN HOWARD PAYNE

SIR HENRY BISHOP

'Mid____ pleas - ures and pal - a - ces,

tho'____ we may roam, Be it ev - er so

hum - ble, there's no____ place like home. A

charm____ from the skies seems to hal - low us

ONE HUNDRED FIFTY-SIX

Dreams of Childhood

ELEANOR THOMPSON

I turned back the hands of time one day,
On a day that was sunny and mild.
In my thoughts I lingered in childhood's vale
And remembered my life as a child.

What pleasures we had on that day long ago,
The kind that were simple and pure.
The best are the ones we never forgot,
The kind that forever endure.

There's the playhouse we made in the old wagon shed
With the cans and the old broken dishes.
How could we forget our grown-up plans,
Our dreams and grown-up wishes?

See that field off there! It's a sea of pure gold,
From a mariner's point of view,
But they really were black-eyed Susans
That we joyfully rambled through.

We took off our shoes and waded the brook;
Who knew . . . but we alone?
There were minnows to catch and dams to build
And the search for a beautiful stone.

Our dreams came and went as the years passed by,
And now they are memories of old.
But years don't turn back and, as day follows day,
Memories are more precious than gold.

All to myself I think of you,
Think of the things we used to do,
Think of the things we used to say,
Think of each happy bygone day.
Sometimes I sigh, and sometimes I smile,
But I keep each olden, golden while.

—WILBUR D. NESBIT

Memories of Home

An Old Homeplace

VIRGINIA BORMAN GRIMMER

Now one can travel miles on end,
Discover wonders at road's bend;
But nothing on this good earth's face
Can charm quite like an old homeplace—

A house where laughter rang in halls
And Mother's bell pealed dinner calls.
The fresh-washed linens hung outdoors,
And folks were happy with their chores.

The home-baked cookies, bread in loaves,
All came with loving hand from stoves.
Quaint crocheted doilies, tatted lace,
All added to the old homeplace.

The cellar room held put-up wares
Like applesauce and golden pears;
At least five hundred quarts it held
Beside black walnuts freshly shelled.

Oh, cities have their own allure
And modern houses are fun to tour;
But in one's memory road to trace,
There's nothing like an old homeplace.

Home

ZENITH HESS

I sometimes dream of a house I knew
Where perfumed roses adorned the view,
Where happy wren songs would often pour
From maple trees by the old back door.
With windows wide, 'twas no place for gloom
When sweet gales drifted from room to room;
And mem'ries filled every corner there
With children's laughter and joy to spare.
Each day was filled with a million things,
The work and play that a lifetime brings.

ONE HUNDRED FIFTY-NINE

INDEX

Titles of poems, prose pieces, and songs are italicized.

Home Sweet Home